ALL NEW
QUICK
CROSSWORDS

Volume 2

The Telegraph

ALL NEW QUICK CROSSWORDS

Volume 2

hamlyn

An Hachette UK Company
www.hachette.co.uk

First published in Great Britain in 2012 by
Hamlyn, a division of Octopus Publishing Group Ltd
Endeavour House, 189 Shaftesbury Avenue
London WC2H 8JY
www.octopusbooks.co.uk

ISBN 978-0-60062-494-3

A CIP catalogue record for this book is available from the British Library.

Printed and bound by CPI Group (UK) Ltd, Croydon, CR0 4YY

1 3 5 7 9 10 8 6 4 2

Acknowledgements
Telegraph Puzzle Editor: Philip McNeill
Editorial Director: Trevor Davies
Senior Editor: Leanne Bryan
Designer: Eoghan O'Brien
Editorial Assistant: Pauline Bache
Page make up: Dorchester Typesetting Group Ltd
Production: Peter Hunt

EDITOR'S NOTE

Welcome to our new collection of Quick Crosswords. There's
no better way to sharpen your wits and widen your vocabulary
than to undertake a good Quick Crossword, and we introduce
150 of them here.

Each day in *The Daily Telegraph*, a different compiler sets the
Cryptic and Quick crosswords as a pair. This helps to give the
puzzles variety as the week goes by, and it should offer a
mixture of styles as you work your way through this book.

One thing to look out for is the pun at the start of each puzzle.
The first two answers (or sometimes the first three, four or five
answers) produce a pun – and the more corny the pun, the
better. For instance, if the first three answers are 'Horse', 'Tray'
and 'Leer', the pun is 'Australia'. The puns are revealed along
with the answers at the back of the book.

Happy solving from everyone in the *Telegraph* crossword team.

Phil McNeill
Telegraph Crossword Editor

Puzzles

1

Across

1 Chair wheel (6)
5 Raise (anchor) (5)
9 Vibration (9)
10 Target score (golf) (3)
11 Noise (3)
12 Those finishing second (7-2)
14 Plan (3)
16 Lingo (anag.) (3,2)
18 Organ of hearing (3)
19 Sails (9)
21 Burnt residue (3)
22 Add (3)
23 Olympic sports (9)
25 Cold dish (5)
26 Motor (6)

Down

2 Fire-raising (5)
3 Extension of a plant (7)
4 Managed (3)
5 In which place (5)
6 Stalemate (7)
7 Payment by instalments (4-8)
8 Prevails (12)
13 Period of darkness (5)
15 Crucial (7)
17 Savings in reserve (4,3)
20 Marvellous (5)
21 Foreign (5)
24 Garden tool (3)

The Telegraph

Across

1 Girls in general... (7)
5 ...and a good-looking one (5)
8 Leg bone (5)
9 Peter –, actor (7)
10 Rile mob (anag.) (7)
11 Chemical in photography (5)
12 New York river (6)
14 Shone (6)
17 Strong flame (5)
19 Cricket officials (7)
22 Rotating (7)
23 Extraterrestrial (5)
24 Having good flavour (5)
25 Contributor to debate (7)

Down

1 Unit of length (5)
2 Drank (7)
3 Lyric muse (5)
4 Sudden storm (6)
5 Distressing (7)
6 Add on by conquest (5)
7 Hung in the air (7)
12 Animal's natural home (7)
13 Fatness to excess (7)
15 Midland county town (7)
16 OT book (6)
18 Tapestry (5)
20 Stage (5)
21 'Mister' in Spain (5)

The Telegraph

3

Across

1 Prickly seedcase (4)
3 Chinese dynasty (4)
6 Son of Noah (3)
9 Midlands city (13)
10 Secretive (8)
12 Cook (4)
13 Expire (3)
15 Rectangular (6)
18 Grab (6)
19 Garment (3)
21 Handle roughly (4)
22 Trial sum (anag.) (8)
25 Safely achieved (5,4,4)
26 Dried grass (3)
27 Ode (4)
28 Mormon state (4)

Down

1 Orally (2,4,2,5)
2 Tiler (anag.) (5)
4 Under control (2,4)
5 Plucky (4)
6 Small axe (7)
7 Best player (3,2,3,5)
8 Pedigree (7)
11 It's (3)
14 Occupy fully (7)
16 Washhouse (7)
17 Indian state (3)
20 Brief look (6)
23 Nitre (anag.) (5)
24 Support (4)

Across

1 – Oldfield, musician (4)
4 Prickly bush (4)
8 Manage (4)
9 Bewildering maze (9)
11 Marsh (6)
13 Young hare (7)
15 Biblical mount (6)
16 Scamp (6)
18 White whale (6)
20 Cushion (6)
22 Topical (anag.) (7)
23 Step down (6)
25 Optimistically (9)
26 Slab of clay (4)
27 Futile (4)
28 Affectedly artistic (4)

Down

2 Fe (4)
3 Devon city (6)
4 Din (6)
5 Season (6)
6 Not a long-distance phone connection (5,4)
7 Curved glass (4)
10 Of the study of plants (7)
12 Doorpost (4)
13 Anarchically (9)
14 Dutch painter (3,4)
17 Lustful (4)
19 Asphyxia (6)
20 Epigon (anag.) (6)
21 Gap (6)
23 Ceremonial act (4)
24 Blemish (4)

5

Across

1 Lure (4)
4 Lout (3)
6 Vase (3)
8 Replacement (12)
10 Booty (6)
12 Belly (6)
13 Identical (5)
14 Gaelic (4)
15 Tumble (4)
17 Sorcery (5)
19 Pretence (6)
21 Selected (6)
23 Seamstress (12)
24 Gab (3)
25 Arid (3)
26 Ooze (4)

Down

2 Watery (7)
3 Scuffle (6)
4 Forget (4)
5 Thrifty (6)
6 League (5)
7 Unconcerned (10)
9 Dominance (10)
11 Crouch (5)
12 Frenzy (5)
16 Ascetic (7)
17 Deceived (6)
18 Refrain (6)
20 Slink (5)
22 Influence (4)

Across

1 Floor (6)
4 Lacking stimulation (5)
8 Plunder (5)
9 Fervent (7)
10 Part of book (7)
11 Festivity (4)
12 Deer (3)
14 Norse saga (4)
15 Reflected sound (4)
18 Record on ship (3)
21 Test (4)
23 Pear-shaped fruit (7)
25 Imaginary animal (7)
26 Additional (5)
27 Very poor (5)
28 Economist (6)

Down

1 Rigorous (6)
2 Brusque (7)
3 Ultimate (8)
4 Bird's bill (4)
5 Spanish wine (5)
6 Dreary (6)
7 Blue (5)
13 Paraffin oil (8)
16 Encourage (7)
17 Spangle (6)
19 Haggard (5)
20 Confused situation (6)
22 Supple (5)
24 Reproduction (4)

7

Across

1 A piece of paper money (4)
3 Units of land measurement (5)
7 Norse deity (4)
8 Intolerable (10)
9 Twenty quires (4)
12 Bungling (11)
13 Sharpened (5)
15 Doorkeeper (5)
19 A fear of open spaces (11)
21 Covered with blood (4)
23 Calm; philosophical (10)
24 Carpets (4)
25 Sailing boat (5)
26 In a tense state (4)

Down

1 Nutritious (10)
2 An unsightly thing (7)
3 Brusque (6)
4 Refund (6)
5 Rear end (5)
6 State of unconsciousness (4)
10 To design on metal (4)
11 Rule by women (10)
14 Close (4)
16 Warehousing (7)
17 Lark about (6)
18 Peg for a vent hole (6)
20 Romany (5)
22 Burden (4)

The Telegraph

Across

1 Devon river (3)
3 Vile dog (3)
5 Eschew (4)
7 Not filled in (5)
8 Old-fashioned exclamation (6)
10 Solemn promise (4)
11 Prediction (8)
13 Fraud (6)
14 Pathos (anag.) (6)
17 Very hungry (8)
19 Psychologist (4)
21 Extensive plain (6)
22 Collier (5)
23 Wilt (4)
24 Transgression (3)
25 Emergency message (3)

Down

1 Decorative needlework (10)
2 Stretch material (7)
3 Fuel (4)
4 Shaving items (6)
5 Carver (8)
6 Excessive (5)
9 Greek mathematician (10)
12 Capital of Manitoba (8)
15 Saintly theologian (7)
16 Coercion (6)
18 Essential (5)
20 Sign (4)

The Telegraph

9

Across

1 Sauce base (4)
4 Hive worker (3)
6 Swindle (3)
8 Photo given too much light (12)
10 Throne (anag.) (6)
12 Warmed (6)
13 Former Egyptian president (5)
14 Sharpen (4)
15 Front of a ship (4)
17 Christian symbol (5)
19 Prime (6)
21 Of aromatic plants (6)
23 Experience poverty (4,3,5)
24 Fox (3)
25 Kernel (3)
26 Melody (4)

Down

2 Head of a coin (7)
3 Ancient Persian king (6)
4 Having a square appearance (4)
5 Missile (6)
6 Rind (5)
7 Good-for-nothing (4-2-4)
9 Gossip (4,3,3)
11 Linger (5)
12 Rough (5)
16 Stream in northern Italy (7)
17 William –, printer (6)
18 Exists (anag.) (6)
20 Relinquish (5)
22 Biblical passage (4)

Across

1 Before (4)
3 Like a hurricane (8)
9 Semi-darkness (5)
10 Blend (7)
11 Depressed (3)
13 Baton (9)
14 Forearm bone (6)
16 Joined (6)
18 Vertically (2-3-4)
20 Early morning moisture (3)
22 Cul-de-sac (4,3)
23 Aspect (5)
25 Urgency (8)
26 Elevated (4)

Down

1 Glean (anag.) (5)
2 Couple (3)
4 Of food, delicious (3-3)
5 Dictionary (7)
6 Disgusted (9)
7 Removed dirt (7)
8 Sooty matter (4)
12 Alert (4,5)
14 Bring together (5,2)
15 Sunders (anag.) (7)
17 Miracle (6)
19 Worthless (4)
21 Hag (5)
24 Greek X (3)

11

Across

1 Irish writer (5)
4 Tedious person (4)
8 Unhurried (7)
9 Serious (5)
10 Weapon (5)
11 Raise (7)
13 Middle (6)
15 Dull (6)
17 Shakespeare hero (7)
20 Hive (5)
22 Fight (5)
23 Whirlwind (7)
24 Nought (4)
25 Elude (5)

Down

1 Part of the UK (5)
2 English county (12)
3 South American country (7)
4 Emblem (5)
5 Scoundrel (5)
6 A Greek dip (12)
7 Vegetable (6)
12 Was ahead (3)
13 Pick (6)
14 Long thin fish (3)
16 Reticence (7)
18 Become void (5)
19 Get the better of (5)
21 Elk (5)

Across

1 One who succeeds (4)
4 Ponder (5)
8 Lack of company (8)
9 Incidental benefit (4)
10 Children's game (1-3)
11 Seeming (8)
12 Coolness (6)
14 Mature (6)
16 Proper (8)
19 Tart (4)
20 Smacker (4)
21 Card game (8)
22 River (5)
23 Worry (4)

Down

2 Girl's name (5)
3 Nonsense (7)
4 Cub (5)
5 Endanger (7)
6 Wading bird (5)
7 Idle chat (6)
13 Small marsupial (7)
14 Dog (7)
15 Fruit (6)
17 Expel (5)
18 Film award (5)
19 Myth (5)

13

Across

1 Metal joint (4)
4 Relax (4)
8 Remedy (4)
9 Citrus preserve (9)
11 Generator (6)
13 Blether (7)
15 Bother (6)
16 Accompany (6)
18 Scottish royal dynasty (6)
20 Public speaker (6)
22 Attractive devices (7)
23 Crawl (6)
25 Degeneracy (9)
26 Underworld river (4)
27 Form of poker (4)
28 Sour tasting (4)

Down

2 Panache (4)
3 Shows reluctance (6)
4 Give an account of (6)
5 Burden (with) (6)
6 Economical cars (9)
7 Refuse to authorise (4)
10 An ugly sight (7)
12 Consequently (4)
13 Alias (9)
14 Frightened (7)
17 Sward (4)
19 Natural ability (6)
20 In a forward direction (6)
21 Bear witness (6)
23 Strong air current (4)
24 Mark of injury (4)

Across

1 Vulgarly pretentious art (6)
4 Hair dye (5)
8 Villain (5)
9 Opponent of progress (7)
10 Met hero (anag.) (7)
11 Cast off (4)
12 Period (3)
14 Jacob's brother (4)
15 Beloved (4)
18 Near the ground (3)
21 Snakes (4)
23 Need (7)
25 Lines of equal pressure (7)
26 Not chronic (5)
27 Space under church (5)
28 Way (6)

Down

1 Form of unarmed combat (6)
2 Female wild cat (7)
3 In good spirits (8)
4 Islamic pilgrimage (4)
5 Horse's noise (5)
6 List of items for meeting (6)
7 Culpability (5)
13 Sufficient (8)
16 Angle in astronomy (7)
17 Insane person (6)
19 Joint (5)
20 Protect (6)
22 Person acting for another (5)
24 Immense (4)

15

Across

1 The god Pluto (3)
3 Operate (8)
9 Passageway (5)
10 Ballroom dance (7)
11 Loo (3)
13 Going bald (4,2,3)
14 Puzzle (6)
16 Lessened (6)
18 Without a will (9)
20 Flop (3)
22 Small-sized newspaper (7)
23 Sword (5)
25 Giving up (8)
26 US sweet potato (3)

Down

1 Slow speech (5)
2 Personification of the sun (3)
4 Inequitable (6)
5 Dandy (7)
6 Vexed (9)
7 Memo-block (4-3)
8 Ait (4)
12 Broccoli e.g. (9)
14 Together (7)
15 Bods can (anag.) (7)
17 Enrage (6)
19 Undemanding (4)
21 Imagine (5)
24 Lad (3)

Across

1 Retail (4)
4 Breezy (4)
8 Literary drudge (4)
9 Completely full (3-6)
11 Abase oneself (6)
13 Always (7)
15 Aide (6)
16 Belittle (2,4)
18 Surrender (4,2)
20 Dearth (anag.) (6)
22 Tried (7)
23 Sea-trip (6)
25 Violently agitated (9)
26 – Canal (4)
27 Ibex (4)
28 Philosophic meditation (4)

Down

2 Test (4)
3 Personal computer (6)
4 Bowman (6)
5 Emitted smoke (6)
6 Education (anag.) (9)
7 Oblique (4)
10 Dot's full name (7)
12 Cormorant (4)
13 Seasoned (9)
14 Demand (7)
17 Naked (4)
19 Spurious (6)
20 Extinct dog (6)
21 Truly (6)
23 Ready money (4)
24 Disadvantage (4)

17

Across

1 Solidifies (7)
5 Aperture (4)
7 Washout (5)
8 Support (6)
10 Munch (4)
11 Anticlimax (8)
13 Powerful (6)
14 Elementary (6)
17 Workout (8)
19 Tangle (4)
21 Saunter (6)
22 Argot (5)
23 Wrath (4)
24 Insanity (7)

Down

1 Chopper (10)
2 Venerate (7)
3 Deserve (4)
4 Flavour (6)
5 Delirium (8)
6 Lariat (5)
9 Catching (10)
12 Yarn (8)
15 Atonement (7)
16 Madhouse (6)
18 Supplement (5)
20 Joyful (4)

Across

1 Strips (5)
4 Put pen to paper (5)
10 Hobby (7)
11 Tubes (5)
12 Waterway (5)
13 Lowered (7)
15 Organ (4)
17 Horses (5)
19 Females (5)
22 Cardinal point (4)
25 Asks (7)
27 Thespian (5)
29 Revel (anag.) (5)
30 Lived (7)
31 Said (5)
32 Demanded (5)

Down

2 Protective clothing (5)
3 In the same way (7)
5 Fast (5)
6 Normal (7)
7 Area (5)
8 Dour (5)
9 Privately (5)
14 Incites (4)
16 Employed (4)
18 Got rid of (7)
20 Slanting print (7)
21 Strangely (5)
23 Remains (5)
24 Occupation (5)
26 Self-possession (5)
28 Appellation of rank (5)

19

Across
1 Parts of shoes (5)
4 Ragamuffin (6)
7 Military officer (7)
8 Tiny particle (4)
10 Bit player (5)
11 Fulfil (7)
14 Disorder (4)
16 Lobbed (6)
18 Cut (6)
21 Toothed wheel (4)
23 Missed out (7)
26 Change (5)
27 Volcanic rock (4)
28 Brass instrument (7)
29 Disposition (6)
30 Unsuccessful one (5)

Down
1 Proposition (10)
2 Longitudinal measures (7)
3 Family appellation (7)
4 Except when (6)
5 Workmanship (5)
6 Metal shackles (5)
9 Hand-operated printer (10)
12 Continent (4)
13 Hostelry (3)
15 Fringe (4)
17 Pose (3)
19 Proceeding in small stages (7)
20 Tentacled cephalopod (7)
22 Press chief (6)
24 Effigy (5)
25 Hobo (5)

Across

- **1** Nail for carpet? (4)
- **4** Venetian artist (6)
- **7** Born as (French) (3)
- **9** Buzz off! (4)
- **10** Petty quarrel (8)
- **11** Amusing person (3)
- **12** Abominable snowman (4)
- **13** Better (8)
- **16** Device for measuring radiation (6,7)
- **19** Seller of gems (8)
- **23** Spicy (4)
- **24** Go wrong (3)
- **25** Fortification (8)
- **26** Noise of pig (4)
- **27** Solemn promise (3)
- **28** Covering for arm (6)
- **29** Crisis of 1956 (4)

Down

- **2** Even a chemist (anag.) (12)
- **3** Being acquainted with (7)
- **4** International matches (5)
- **5** Heavy blow (5)
- **6** Brownish yellow (5)
- **8** Light-emitting property (12)
- **14** Male family member (5)
- **15** Flightless bird (3)
- **17** Measure of cloth (3)
- **18** Loses width (7)
- **20** Surpass (5)
- **21** Rental contract (5)
- **22** Magistrate (historical) (5)

21

Across

1 Odour (5)
8 Swiss cheese (8)
9 Fairness (7)
10 Narrow and pointed (8)
11 Condiment (7)
12 Two pints (5)
15 Axeman (5)
18 Arrange feathers (5)
19 Wireless (5)
22 Change direction (7)
23 Rattlesnake (3,5)
24 Nicotine plant (7)
25 Old rover (anag.) (8)
26 Bullock (5)

Down

2 Crossbearer (8)
3 Talked idly (8)
4 Smudge (5)
5 Tomato sauce (7)
6 Eminence (7)
7 Transparency (5)
8 Showy display (5)
13 Proud (8)
14 Feeler (8)
16 Fairground roundabout (7)
17 Ludicrous (7)
20 NT king (5)
21 Ladle (5)
22 Hear case again (5)

The Telegraph

Across

7 Register (information) (4,2)
8 Food fish (6)
9 It lies with the prosecution (6,2,5)
10 Greek lamb dish (8)
12 Bouquet (4)
13 Body mark (4)
15 One very famous (8)
17 Eventually commit oneself (4,3,6)
19 Capsicum (6)
20 Marsh (6)

Down

1 Singer Enrico (6)
2 Completely (in love) (4,4,5)
3 Soon (4)
4 Excellent (8)
5 All above board (4-3-6)
6 Over (6)
11 Furniture item (8)
14 Dance (3-3)
16 Majestic (6)
18 Light shoe (4)

23

Across

1 Armed conflict (3)
3 Territory (4)
5 Deserve (4)
8 Order (8)
10 Oval fruit (4)
11 Faucet (3)
13 Body part (5)
14 Canteen (9)
16 Beer (3)
17 Rodent (3)
19 Behaviour (9)
21 Christmas song (5)
22 Payment (3)
24 Row (4)
25 Permissive (8)
26 Recess (4)
27 Part of the eye (4)
28 Firearm (3)

Down

1 Delay action (4)
2 File (4)
3 Whirling dance (10)
4 Clergyman (6)
6 Parable (8)
7 Propose (8)
9 Maritime (5)
12 Lack of refinement (10)
14 Indian city (8)
15 Bold (8)
18 Foreign (5)
20 Good turn (6)
22 Tooth (4)
23 Public school (4)

The Telegraph

Across

1 Schoolgirl (4)
5 Water grass (4)
7 Raise (7)
8 Dilapidated (8)
10 Eject (4)
12 Metal (4)
14 Mysterious (8)
16 Tonic (4-2-2)
17 Enslave (4)
18 Net (4)
19 Moroccan port (8)
22 Succinct in speech (7)
23 Bird of prey (4)
24 Entertainer of guests (4)

Down

1 Atmosphere (4)
2 Brand (4)
3 Italian cheese (3,5)
4 Enormous (4)
5 Convalescence (8)
6 Silly (4)
9 Building (7)
11 Gummed label (7)
13 Mouth (slang) (4,4)
15 Adversary (8)
18 Deride (4)
19 Diplomacy (4)
20 Teasing desire (4)
21 Opening (4)

25

Across

1 Rescind (decision) (7)
5 Conceal (4)
7 Kitchen wear (5)
8 Relaxed (6)
10 Overlook (4)
11 Presiding official (8)
13 For a short time (6)
14 Cask (6)
17 Paid attention (8)
19 Bits of information (4)
21 Wooden huts (6)
22 Crockery (5)
23 Wad of tobacco (4)
24 Have doubts about (7)

Down

1 Not excessive or extreme (10)
2 Protective coating (7)
3 Relative status (4)
4 Hearts (anag.) (6)
5 Infirmary (8)
6 Aspire (5)
9 Obnoxious (10)
12 Dormant (8)
15 Understand (7)
16 Stops (6)
18 Kiosk (5)
20 Freezes (4)

Across

1 Staffed (6)
4 River islands (4)
9 Portrayed (5)
10 Porch (7)
11 Study (7)
12 Skilful (5)
13 Badly worn (6)
15 Hindu retreat (6)
18 Small and elegant (5)
20 Beard named after painter (7)
23 Listless (7)
24 Create (5)
25 Loathe (4)
26 Connective tissue (6)

Down

1 Insect (5)
2 North American river (7)
3 Boredom (5)
5 Encroachments (7)
6 Grab (5)
7 Rate of progress (5)
8 Drum (3-3)
13 Understated (6)
14 Bunch of flowers (7)
16 Name for fox (7)
17 Dodge (5)
19 Prophet swallowed by whale (5)
21 Recess (5)
22 Dine at home (5)

27

Across

1 Madagascan primate (5)
4 Read (6)
7 Home of the US Congress (7)
8 Border on (4)
10 What rubbish! (2,3)
11 Complicated (7)
14 Clearing of throat (4)
16 Until now (2,4)
18 Barometric curve (6)
21 Delayed (4)
23 Essentially (7)
26 Impish (5)
27 Wisecrack (4)
28 Capital of Corsica (7)
29 Clever trick (6)
30 – Marner (George Eliot novel) (5)

Down

1 Railway engine (10)
2 One with unkempt hair (7)
3 Recede (7)
4 Civil force (6)
5 Empire (5)
6 Cranium (5)
9 Not belonging (10)
12 Leave out (4)
13 For (3)
15 Underworld (4)
17 – Gardner, actress (3)
19 Playground games (7)
20 Lens with two prescriptions (7)
22 1 across (3-3)
24 Contact (5)
25 Slip (5)

The Telegraph

Across

4 Cold (6)
5 Nose (slang) (4)
7 Books of tickets (7)
10 Unrefined (5)
11 Senator (anag.) (7)
12 Post of winding stairs (5)
14 By now (7)
15 Capital of Ecuador (5)
16 Provoke to anger (7)
20 Fetch (5)
21 Crescent-shaped ornament (7)
22 Bantu warrior (4)
23 Crustacean (6)

Down

1 Goliath (5)
2 Wind instrument (5)
3 Trek (7)
4 Wheedle (4)
6 Renal organ (6)
8 Soon (3,4)
9 Miser (4-3)
10 Censure (7)
13 Crystal (6)
14 Feeling thrilled (7)
17 Anything (Shakespearean) (5)
18 Weird (5)
19 Pace (4)

29

Across

- **7** Damage (6)
- **8** Idea (6)
- **10** Allow (7)
- **11** Steeple (5)
- **12** Preserve (4)
- **13** Pariah (5)
- **17** Artificial (5)
- **18** Twist (4)
- **22** Transparent (5)
- **23** Preview (7)
- **24** Talisman (6)
- **25** Planet (6)

Down

- **1** Aversion (7)
- **2** Expelled (7)
- **3** Trademark (5)
- **4** Ogre (7)
- **5** Stiff (5)
- **6** Seraph (5)
- **9** Requirement (9)
- **14** Wed (7)
- **15** Wreath (7)
- **16** Subjugate (7)
- **19** Vamoose (5)
- **20** Christ (5)
- **21** Sprite (5)

Across

1 Hot season (6)
5 See 25
9 Source of zest (5,4)
10 Scots expression of impatience (3)
11 Tin (3)
12 Elated (4-1-4)
14 See 21
16 Silly-billy (5)
18 Weight (3)
19 Strictly (2,7)
21 & 14 Ozone (3,3)
22 Young fellow (3)
23 Where hops are dried (4,5)
25 & 5 Purgative medicine (5,5)
26 Centre (6)

Down

2 Emasculate (5)
3 Tailless pet (4,3)
4 Fish eggs (3)
5 Chilli sauce (5)
6 Sentry (7)
7 Philosopher – punches a hero (anag.) (12)
8 Battered (5,3,4)
13 Greek island (5)
15 Altar screen (7)
17 Very dry (7)
20 New husband (5)
21 Case for brain (5)
24 Total (3)

31

Across

1 Oven-cook (4)
3 Makes a mistake (4)
9 Unexpected surprise (5)
10 Irregular fighter (9)
11 Hurl (5)
12 In another place (9)
15 Stealing (6)
17 Method of working (6)
19 Set up (9)
21 Bare (5)
23 Book repositories (9)
24 Revolution (5)
25 Viewed (4)
26 Aeons (4)

Down

1 French loaf (8)
2 Souvenir (8)
4 Respite (6)
5 Formal; type of home (7)
6 Close (4)
7 Cook in liquid (4)
8 Increase (4)
13 Impressive (8)
14 Stress (8)
16 Goads (7)
18 Bleats (anag.) (6)
20 Smile broadly (4)
21 Purloin (slang) (4)
22 Recoil of gun (4)

Across

1 More astute (7)
8 Conjunction indicating choice (7)
9 Bohemian dance (5)
10 Territories won in war (9)
11 Tree (3)
12 Girl's name; heath (5)
13 Picky (5)
14 Meat from pig (5)
16 Informal language (5)
19 Beard of plant (3)
20 Italian composer (9)
22 Special lineage (5)
23 Post via plane (7)
24 Carry out (7)

Down

1 Army engineer (6)
2 Intensity of sound (6)
3 Lack of anything being done (8)
4 African country (6)
5 OT chariot-driver (4)
6 Spooks (6)
7 Reliable (6)
13 Base life (anag.) (8)
14 Pandemonium (6)
15 Bird (6)
16 Resolve (6)
17 Rich cake (6)
18 Nervy (2,4)
21 Great eagerness (4)

The Telegraph

33

Across

1 Gave support (6)
4 Weirder (6)
9 Science (5)
10 Military clothes (7)
11 Inn (3)
12 Overturn (5)
13 Light roll (7)
15 Changing into vapour (11)
19 Communist (7)
20 Pleasure trip (5)
21 Expression of surprise (3)
22 Space to stretch (7)
24 Skunk-like animal (5)
25 Adjust (6)
26 Crossbred (6)

Down

1 Inflate (4,2)
2 Change loyalty (5,4)
3 North-east African country (5)
5 Its tile (anag.) (7)
6 Wedding vow (1,2)
7 IOM town (6)
8 Approve (6-5)
14 Winner (9)
16 Form couples (4,3)
17 Symbol (6)
18 Unemotional (6)
20 Flashy (5)
23 Deity (3)

The Telegraph

Across

1 Defender (4)
4 Rank (4)
8 Bring up (4)
9 Two weeks (9)
11 Blood vessel (6)
13 Bacteria (7)
15 Impotence drug (6)
16 Wickedly (6)
18 Shy (6)
20 Client (6)
22 Wheeled basket (7)
23 Cream cake (6)
25 Light-fingered (9)
26 Circle (4)
27 Dust (anag.) (4)
28 Dimensions (4)

Down

2 Affirm (4)
3 Knapsack (6)
4 Woman's name (dim.) (6)
5 Breathe out (6)
6 Gems (9)
7 Low cart (4)
10 Petty (7)
12 Egg (4)
13 Musicians' platform (9)
14 Cut glass (7)
17 Jerk (4)
19 Shirker (6)
20 Calm (6)
21 Sent in (anag.) (6)
23 Bug (4)
24 Test of knowledge (4)

Across

1 Upper limit (7)
8 Defeats heavily (6)
9 List (7)
11 Calm (8)
12 US actress, – Dunne (5)
14 Animal flesh (4)
15 Greek god of the sea (8)
17 Lawyer (8)
18 Guide (4)
20 Incorrect (5)
21 Roomy (8)
23 Smash (7)
24 Records (6)
25 Breathing space (7)

Down

2 Whole (6)
3 Mourn (6)
4 Cosy retreat (4)
5 Duct (7)
6 Rogue (9)
7 Walkway by the sea (9)
10 Wrong (9)
12 Expressionless (9)
13 Towards the Orient (9)
16 Betrayer (7)
18 Portable computer (6)
19 Agreement (6)
22 Footwear item (4)

The Telegraph

36

Across
1 Amount of paper (5)
4 Hearten (4)
8 Complaint (7)
9 Pointed extension of leaf (5)
10 Instrument (5)
11 Genuine (7)
13 Answer sharply (6)
15 Evoke (6)
17 Unite (7)
20 Distant (5)
22 Heading (5)
23 Small scrap (7)
24 Dam (4)
25 Circumference (5)

Down
1 Ecuadorian capital (5)
2 Improper (12)
3 Name used in Beatles song (7)
4 Foundation (5)
5 Frequently (5)
6 Have a fall (4,1,7)
7 Devise (6)
12 Formality (3)
13 Repeat from memory (6)
14 Light brown (3)
16 Tendency (7)
18 Sluggish (5)
19 Racecourse (5)
21 Bring (5)

37

Across

1 Dramatic work (4)
3 Posh people (5)
7 Circular band (4)
8 Typecast (10)
9 Ambience; vibes (4)
12 Intruders (11)
13 Rub out (5)
15 Prevaricate; boundary (5)
19 Husbandry (11)
21 International currency (4)
23 Enterprise (10)
24 Scheme (4)
25 Cunning (5)
26 Sedimentary deposit (4)

Down

1 Plague (10)
2 Cricket deliveries (7)
3 Mythical Scandinavian cave dwellers (6)
4 Big breakfasts! (3-3)
5 Fleece (5)
6 Acidic (4)
10 Secondhand (4)
11 Forerunner (10)
14 At a distance (4)
16 Landed properties (7)
17 Bathing costume (6)
18 Fruitless (6)
20 Departing (5)
22 Deficient in beauty (4)

Across

1 Item of jewellery (6)
4 Further down (5)
8 Diarist Samuel (5)
9 Deadlock (7)
10 Constrict (7)
11 Restaurant list (4)
12 Bob the head (3)
14 Type of cheese (4)
15 Like 2,4,6, ... (4)
18 Heavens above! (3)
21 Wind instrument (4)
23 Burdensome (7)
25 Bread roll (7)
26 Food; nonsense (5)
27 Laconic (5)
28 Handsome youth (6)

Down

1 Road around town (6)
2 Planet (7)
3 Gambling centre in USA (3,5)
4 Move with long strides (4)
5 Sweat (anag.) (5)
6 – monkey (6)
7 Female fox (5)
13 Downcast (8)
16 Process of wearing away (7)
17 Water ice (6)
19 Bumpkin (5)
20 Put a value on (6)
22 Willow twig (5)
24 Point of maximum
   development (4)

The Telegraph

39

Across

- **1** Over (4)
- **4** Fixed (4)
- **8** King's – (4)
- **9** Harmful (9)
- **11** Lady of Spain (6)
- **13** Said (7)
- **15** Thin coating (6)
- **16** Frustrated (6)
- **18** Air attack (6)
- **20** Streamer (6)
- **22** Late (7)
- **23** Swindle (6)
- **25** Ideal romantic partner (9)
- **26** Fled (4)
- **27** Cor! (4)
- **28** Raspberry (slang); jeer (US) (4)

Down

- **2** Pig's noise (4)
- **3** Compare (6)
- **4** More equitable (6)
- **5** Soured (anag.) (6)
- **6** Percussion instrument (9)
- **7** Old Indian coin (4)
- **10** Drugged (7)
- **12** Rara –, rare bird; or car rental firm (4)
- **13** Unrestrained (9)
- **14** x10 (7)
- **17** Dip biscuit in drink (4)
- **19** Very much (4,2)
- **20** Sermonise (6)
- **21** Integer (6)
- **23** St Andrews area (4)
- **24** Joan –, folk singer (4)

Across

1 Change (5)
4 Tranquillity (5)
10 Italian white wine (7)
11 Over-stimulated (5)
12 Arm bones (5)
13 Composer (7)
15 Underworld river (4)
17 Heavy pole (5)
19 Smaller map (5)
22 As far as (2,2)
25 Palpitate (7)
27 Drive forward (5)
29 Find time for (3,2)
30 Calling up (7)
31 Core (5)
32 Stop (5)

Down

2 Very angry (5)
3 Write mournfully (7)
5 Upper air (5)
6 Overturn (7)
7 Directors (5)
8 Dunce (5)
9 Feed on grass (5)
14 Way out (4)
16 Faithful (4)
18 Rather (1,6)
20 Offensive (7)
21 Rigid (5)
23 Is nosey (5)
24 Reflective poem (5)
26 Radio adjuster (5)
28 Great care taken (5)

41

Across

1 Concur (5)
4 Avoid (4)
7 Deserve (4)
8 Rude (8)
9 Blizzard (9)
10 Wager (3)
12 Confirm (6)
14 Generous (6)
16 Ancient (3)
18 Savage (9)
21 Irksome (8)
22 Promise (4)
23 Ray (4)
24 Undressed (5)

Down

1 Versus (7)
2 Illustrious (8)
3 Survive (5)
4 Brood (4)
5 Loosen (5)
6 Coil (6)
11 Disregard (8)
13 Calamitous (6)
15 Stung (7)
17 Thrust (5)
19 Commence (5)
20 Lather (4)

Across

1 Crack in rock (7)
5 Vile (4)
7 Snow leopard; weight (5)
8 Allow (6)
10 Frolic (4)
11 Sketches (8)
13 Published (6)
14 Food staple (6)
17 Jointly (8)
19 Cab (4)
21 Arcs (6)
22 Robbery (5)
23 Mend (4)
24 Let down gently (7)

Down

1 Steps (10)
2 Open footwear (7)
3 Secondhand (4)
4 Proficient (6)
5 Kindling (8)
6 Marriage (5)
9 Linked (10)
12 Fete (8)
15 Unpaid practitioner (7)
16 Boat; container (6)
18 Medical dressing (5)
20 Ragout (4)

43

Across

1 Sham (6)
4 Masterstroke (4)
8 Not attending (6)
9 Small farmer (6)
10 Language (5)
11 Private soldier (7)
13 You (arch.) (4)
15 Half a dozen (3)
16 Content of hourglass (4)
18 Hidden (7)
20 Angry (5)
23 Wake up (4,2)
24 Lay waste (6)
25 Look after (the sick) (4)
26 No longer a teenager (6)

Down

1 Bagpipe music (7)
2 Improve by altering (5)
3 Go out with (4)
5 Fragrant (7)
6 Aircraft (5)
7 Acting for another (2,5)
12 Actor Peter (7)
14 Indefinitely large in number (7)
17 Old-fashioned posy (7)
19 Henhouse (5)
21 Black bird (5)
22 Make tea or beer (4)

Across

7 Thumped (6)
8 Muncher (6)
9 Celebration after 50 years (6,7)
10 Disregarding with contempt (8)
12 Sun, Mon, Tues, ... (4)
13 Dodgy dealer (4)
15 Refuse vehicle (8)
17 In a damaging manner (13)
19 Church officer (6)
20 French novelist (6)

Down

1 Gentle walk (6)
2 Group of four rulers (13)
3 Outer layer (4)
4 Whips (8)
5 Arrangement of chemical elements (8,5)
6 Unorthodox belief (6)
11 Wanted (2,6)
14 Like better (6)
16 Encumber again (6)
18 Toffs (4)

The Telegraph

45

Across

1 Evergreen used in wreaths (5)
4 Principal (4)
7 Lisa (anag.), another girl's name (4)
8 Welsh island (8)
9 Imprisoning (9)
10 Pigpen (3)
12 Lane (6)
14 Geneva (anag.) (6)
16 – of the Covenant (3)
18 Chomp (9)
21 Stringed instrument (8)
22 Find by groping (4)
23 Occident (4)
24 Cymru (5)

Down

1 Study of past events (7)
2 Jumping game (8)
3 Pine (5)
4 Be mindful of (4)
5 Skilful (5)
6 Timetable (6)
11 Compassionate (8)
13 Expression of dismay (4,2)
15 Cowardly (7)
17 Stir up (5)
19 Hurl (5)
20 Caledonian (4)

The Telegraph

Across

1 Young hen (7)
8 Telegraph instrument (6)
9 Sicilian wine (7)
11 Suspension (8)
12 Revolt (5)
14 Enough (archaic) (4)
15 Heated cloth (8)
17 Coarse jesting (8)
18 Thunder-god (4)
20 Pier (5)
21 Abandoning (8)
23 Instruction (7)
24 Sticky (6)
25 25 cents (7)

Down

2 Bliss (6)
3 Acajou (6)
4 – Fitzgerald, jazz singer (4)
5 Two-wheeled vehicle (7)
6 Close-fitting (9)
7 Store in a cold vacuum (6-3)
10 Detestable (9)
12 Procedure (anag.) (9)
13 Practical joke (5,4)
16 Old form of chemistry (7)
18 Canopy; examiner (6)
19 Superfluous (6)
22 Spiritual teacher (4)

47

Across

1 European country (6)
4 Prohibited (6)
7 Complete (8)
9 Non-believer (7)
12 Fragment (5)
13 Disgusting (5)
15 Trapeze (5)
16 Separated (5)
17 Composition (5)
18 Severe (5)
19 Go back over (7)
23 Recommend (8)
24 Be present at (6)
25 Run naked (6)

Down

1 City on the Severn (10)
2 Devotee (10)
3 Card game (8)
4 Cask (4)
5 Facial part (4)
6 Greek god of love (4)
8 Clumsy (3-6)
10 Perfect (10)
11 Type of sweater (10)
14 Idler (8)
20 Way out (4)
21 Ploy (4)
22 Eccentric (4)

The Telegraph

Across

1 Flowerless plant (4)
3 Essence (6)
8 Astonishing (7)
9 Make fun of (5)
10 Relating to mankind (5)
11 Three-pronged spear (7)
12 Buy back (6)
14 Written message (6)
18 Breed of cat (7)
20 Fish (5)
22 Pronounce (5)
23 Attribute (7)
24 Marked (6)
25 Draw together (4)

Down

1 Plumage (7)
2 Kingdom (5)
3 Nullify (6)
4 All (mus.) (5)
5 Substance for chemical test (7)
6 One's betrothed (6)
7 Opening (4)
13 Extreme (7)
15 Tempt (6)
16 Withdrawal (7)
17 Claim (6)
18 Liquid food (4)
19 Mistake (5)
21 Edible bulb (5)

49

Across

1 Sit (as model) (4)
4 Sweets (7)
8 Upright (8)
9 Atmosphere (3)
11 Eating (6)
13 Pattern (6)
14 Tertiary (5)
15 Objectives (4)
17 Maintained (4)
18 Employing (5)
20 Natural gift (6)
21 Pot for boiling (6)
24 Equipment (3)
25 Annoy (8)
26 Fulfil requirements (7)
27 Viewed (4)

Down

2 Body of water (5)
3 Range (6)
4 Mark as correct (4)
5 Doubled over (6)
6 Analyse (7)
7 Fortify (10)
10 Escapades (10)
12 Spirit (5)
13 Inebriated (5)
16 Joy (7)
18 Loosens laces (6)
19 Mild (6)
22 Legal ownership (5)
23 Quarry (4)

50

Across

1 Parrot's name (5)
4 Pollen containers (7)
8 Faster (7)
9 Award (5)
10 Yobbish violence (5)
11 Road material (7)
13 Food (Yiddish) (4)
15 Sluggishness (6)
17 Shun (6)
20 Protuberance (4)
22 Shoves (7)
24 Black bird (5)
26 Item of info (5)
27 Tiredness (7)
28 Mexican salamander (7)
29 Paces (5)

Down

1 Spicy (7)
2 Telling fibs (5)
3 John Lennon's second wife (4,3)
4 Large arteries (6)
5 Restore to full (3,2)
6 Text on gravestone (7)
7 Perspiration (5)
12 One of Noah's sons (4)
14 Heraldic border (4)
16 Rice dish (7)
18 Elves or fairies (7)
19 Curiosities (7)
21 Functional (6)
22 Biblical land (5)
23 Place of uncertain waiting (5)
25 Imprecise (5)

The Telegraph

51

Across

1 Fool (3)
3 Faint (3)
5 Mild expletive (4)
7 Available now (5)
8 Scholarly person (6)
10 Operatic song (4)
11 Indian prince (8)
13 A manse (anag.) (6)
14 Sagebrush State (6)
17 Jelly from seaweed (4-4)
19 Facts (4)
21 Woolly mammal (6)
22 Roasting framework (abbrev.) (3-1-1)
23 Father (4)
24 Also called (abbrev.) (3)
25 – West, actress (3)

Down

1 RAF officer (3-7)
2 Staying power (7)
3 Methods (4)
4 Capital of the Bahamas (6)
5 Turned aside (8)
6 Heavenly food (5)
9 Decorated bier (10)
12 Polynesian skirt (4-4)
15 Letter puzzle (7)
16 North African desert (6)
18 Town near Stirling (5)
20 Swedish pop group (4)

Across

1 South American ostrich (4)
4 Inventory (4)
8 Sound of a clock (4)
9 Fast foxtrot (9)
11 Hazy light; a slight cloudiness (6)
13 Russian composer (7)
15 Old silver coin (6)
16 William –, printer (6)
18 Largest country (6)
20 Transversely (6)
22 Diviner (anag.) (5-2)
23 Catchy rhyme (6)
25 Child (9)
26 Nuisance (4)
27 Labyrinth (4)
28 Copse (4)

Down

2 Pull (4)
3 Charon (anag.); Styx ferryman (6)
4 School period (6)
5 Picturesque (6)
6 Location (9)
7 Lady's fingers (4)
10 Self-punishment (7)
12 At a distance (4)
13 Despotism; a high-handed manner (9)
14 Stiffly (7)
17 Curious (4)
19 Slightly sunken spot (6)
20 Gain retribution (6)
21 It cuts along the grain (6)
23 Jest, joke (4)
24 Prohibit (4)

53

Across

1 Appeal (4)
3 Blemish (4)
9 Secrete (5)
10 Meal (9)
11 Majestic (5)
12 Frequency (9)
15 Suppose (6)
17 Reek (6)
19 Cyclone (9)
21 Imbibed (5)
23 Counterfeit (9)
24 Euphoria (5)
25 Observe (4)
26 Retained (4)

Down

1 Landlord (8)
2 Training (8)
4 Shackles (6)
5 Withdraw (7)
6 Rage (4)
7 Recount (4)
8 Slide (4)
13 Boundless (8)
14 Mystery (8)
16 Soppy (7)
18 Manly (6)
20 Mortgage (4)
21 Obligation (4)
22 Waterless (4)

Across

1 Middle part of body (5)
4 Fragrant herb (5)
10 Master (7)
11 Set in a row (5)
12 Artist's frame (5)
13 Close of the day (7)
15 In addition (4)
17 Aida, e.g. (5)
19 Understands (5)
22 Concept (4)
25 Compound involving two oxygen atoms (7)
27 Cattle farm (5)
29 Gate-keeper's cottage (5)
30 Provided remedies for (7)
31 Recurring series (5)
32 Read up on (5)

Down

2 Graceful horses (5)
3 Student (7)
5 Shore (anag.) (5)
6 Fixing (7)
7 Say (5)
8 Attempts (5)
9 Ridge or shelf (5)
14 Ballot (4)
16 Spread (4)
18 With haughtiness (7)
20 Most hot (7)
21 Strangely (5)
23 Mortality (5)
24 Partial darkness (5)
26 Perfect (5)
28 Eminent (5)

55

Across

1 Unable to move or resist motion (5)
4 Staple food (4)
8 Quick swim (3)
9 Pirate (9)
10 Monster (4)
11 Unable to relax (8)
12 Form of fossil fuel (3)
13 Merely (6)
14 Drops a line (6)
16 Possesses (3)
17 More than adequate (8)
18 Yield (4)
20 Expand (upon) (9)
21 Finish (3)
22 Wight, Man or Skye (4)
23 Also-ran (5)

Down

1 Within a building (7)
2 Used as a trial (12)
3 Big tents (4)
4 Lifts (6)
5 Episodes (8)
6 All the same (12)
7 Weapons (4)
11 Beam (3)
12 Resplendent (8)
14 Used to be (3)
15 Slight in form (7)
16 Compassionate (6)
17 Valley (4)
19 Scream (4)

The Telegraph

Across

1 Gaffer (4)
4 German city (7)
8 Collection of miscellanea (5,3)
9 Little sleep (3)
11 Parts of a gallon (6)
13 Star in Aquila (6)
14 Run away to wed (5)
15 Span (4)
17 Greek philosopher (4)
18 Loose garment (5)
20 Cover (financially) (6)
21 Someone paid for work (6)
24 Fish eggs (3)
25 Rehearsal (8)
26 Merit (7)
27 Require (4)

Down

2 Board for seances (5)
3 Lithe (6)
4 Tramp (4)
5 Slight worry (6)
6 Wine of a good year (7)
7 Range of works performed (10)
10 Wasted (10)
12 Oleaginous (5)
13 At speed (5)
16 Boxes for money (7)
18 Military engineer (6)
19 Type of cloak (6)
22 Cosy corner? (5)
23 Vigil for the dead (4)

57

Across

1 Part (5)
5 Concur (5)
8 Intended (5)
9 Furnish (5)
10 Old coin (9)
11 Make a legal claim (3)
12 Worsen (11)
15 South-west England (4,7)
19 Belonging to us (3)
20 Showy style (9)
22 Antelope (5)
23 Louse (anag.); blackbird (5)
24 Genuflect (5)
25 Like yellow part of egg (5)

Down

1 Erotic entertainment (8)
2 Sweated (6)
3 Forceful (8)
4 Mariner (6)
5 On the summit (4)
6 Kigali's country (6)
7 Irritable (4)
13 Dull-wittedly (8)
14 Ordinary (8)
16 Make a hissing sound while frying (6)
17 Anxiety (6)
18 Informal pronoun in USA (3-3)
20 Lifting device (4)
21 Object of worship (4)

The Telegraph

Across

1 Blame (anag.), lady's name (5)
4 Village (6)
9 English city (7)
10 Perpendicular (5)
11 Tranquil (4)
12 Making inroads (7)
13 Ocean (3)
14 Team (4)
16 Demented (4)
18 Large vehicle (3)
20 Drastic (7)
21 Explosive devices (4)
24 Heavenly body (5)
25 Clear quartz (7)
26 In the last – (6)
27 Inconsiderate speed (5)

Down

1 Ill-will (6)
2 Trite (5)
3 Appear (4)
5 Electioneering platform (8)
6 Staggering around (7)
7 Anger (6)
8 Below (5)
13 Corselet (anag.) (8)
15 Neck of land (7)
17 Swordsman (6)
18 Shore (5)
19 Unskilled worker (6)
22 School subject (5)
23 Legend (4)

59

Across

1 Thomas –, poet (4)
3 Ribbon (4)
9 Mother-of-pearl (5)
10 A soft blue cheese (9)
11 Send in payment (5)
12 Begin (9)
15 Freedom (6)
17 Straight man (6)
19 Unwilling (9)
21 Latin American dance (5)
23 Board game (9)
24 Pleasing view (5)
25 Armoured vehicle (4)
26 Nervous (4)

Down

1 Grotesque waterspout (8)
2 Came to possess (8)
4 Waterproof jacket (6)
5 Implore (7)
6 Dishonest scheme (4)
7 Compass point (4)
8 Abominable snowman (4)
13 Inappropriately named (2-6)
14 Tough (8)
16 Tumbler (7)
18 Large bottle (6)
20 Quote (4)
21 Change address (4)
22 Haze (4)

Across

1 Express contentment (4)
4 Game (5)
8 Disparage (8)
9 Dubious (4)
10 Remain (4)
11 Imaginary (8)
12 Sleeplike state (6)
14 Sprain (6)
16 Crime (8)
19 Sleeveless cloak (4)
20 Equitable (4)
21 Ornament for the wrist (8)
22 Avoid (5)
23 Trick (4)

Down

2 Togetherness (5)
3 Train (7)
4 Surmount (5)
5 Distinctive incident (7)
6 Bulgarian capital (5)
7 Bully (6)
13 African country (7)
14 Capricious (7)
15 Nonentity (6)
17 Custom (5)
18 Walk in a leisurely way (5)
19 Vulgar (5)

61

Across

1 Laugh quietly (7)
5 Abhors (5)
8 Something that happens (5)
9 Function (7)
10 Enigmas (9)
12 Sick (3)
13 Withstand (6)
14 An amount of time (6)
17 Social insect (3)
18 Mishaps (9)
20 Whole number (7)
21 Foe (5)
23 Conceals (5)
24 Sickness (7)

Down

1 Ointment (5)
2 Employ (3)
3 Young cats (7)
4 Strikingly strange (6)
5 Takes notice of (5)
6 Custom (9)
7 Puffed up (7)
11 Believed to be guilty (9)
13 Nonsense (7)
15 Incessant (7)
16 Frightened (6)
18 Kindly protection (5)
19 Fashion (5)
22 Geological period (3)

The Telegraph

Across

1 Bank document (6)
4 Directions on compass (6)
7 Not table d'hôte (1,2,5)
9 Modernised (7)
12 A greyish brown (5)
13 Wine (5)
15 Spiny shrub (5)
16 Of the country (5)
17 Small branch (5)
18 Remove weapons from (5)
19 Players of records (7)
23 Fervid (8)
24 Orson – (6)
25 Not moving (6)

Down

1 Categorised (10)
2 Infuriate (10)
3 Warn Esau (anag.) (8)
4 Secret look (4)
5 State of U.SA (4)
6 Capture (4)
8 Emblem of Henry VIII (5,4)
10 Jousting contest (10)
11 Tactful (10)
14 Line of reasoning (8)
20 European river (4)
21 Prison (4)
22 – Saint-Laurent (4)

The Telegraph

63

Across

1 Modern (3)
3 Pluto (3)
5 Deciduous tree (5)
8 Back tooth (5)
9 Odd (7)
10 Stun (4)
11 Bit (8)
13 Sleeveless jacket (6)
14 Peeping Tom (6)
17 Yearly (3,5)
19 Agitation (4)
22 Passenger vehicle (7)
23 Flat (5)
24 Verse (5)
25 Increase (3)
26 No (3)

Down

1 Wanderer (5)
2 Roundabout (7)
3 Dismal (4)
4 Writhe (6)
5 Heavy stick (8)
6 Ooze out (5)
7 Lost her (anag.) (7)
12 Summit (8)
13 Planet (7)
15 Animate (7)
16 Rabbit hole (6)
18 At hand (5)
20 Friendly (5)
21 Constant change (4)

Across

4 Exposing (6)
7 Direct (8)
8 Imaginary place (6)
10 Need (7)
11 Close up (4)
13 Joyful celebration (8)
14 Join metal (4)
16 Male voice (4)
18 Negotiate (8)
19 On one occasion (4)
21 Metal casing in engine (7)
22 Eradicate (6)
24 Crazy person (8)
25 Slightly drunk (6)

Down

1 Heavenly (8)
2 Estimation (9)
3 Make worse (9)
4 Energy unit related to Fahrenheit (1,1,1)
5 Puncture (6)
6 Fitted with glass (6)
9 Draw (3)
11 Unprincipled man (slang) (9)
12 Filled with reverential fear (9)
15 Escolars (anag.) (8)
16 Regulate (6)
17 Scorching (6)
20 Dove's call (3)
23 Your (3)

65

Across

1 Seabird (3)
3 Certain (4)
5 Close (4)
8 Ominous (8)
10 Behaves (4)
11 Downcast (3)
13 Mature (5)
14 Likeness (9)
16 Nose (3)
17 Racket (3)
19 Careless (9)
21 Garret (5)
22 Plus (3)
24 Filch (4)
25 Shirk (8)
26 Dimwit (4)
27 Niggardly (4)
28 Dull (3)

Down

1 Weaponry (4)
2 Generous (4)
3 Juiciness (10)
4 Fame (6)
6 Adventure (8)
7 Booming (8)
9 Impatient (5)
12 Forecast (10)
14 Ricked (8)
15 Occult (8)
18 Vacuous (5)
20 Revolve (6)
22 Geriatric (4)
23 Tot (4)

Across

1 Card game; the 'smallest room' (3)
3 Aquatic mammal (4)
5 Weep noisily (4)
8 Sheath (8)
10 Avoid deliberately (4)
11 Every single one (3)
13 Board game (5)
14 Of the South Pole (9)
16 Afternoon meal (3)
17 Deciduous tree (3)
19 Restaurant (9)
21 Gatehouse (5)
22 Period of history (3)
24 Ancient city (4)
25 US luxury car (8)
26 Young child's bed (4)
27 Farm building (4)
28 Hatchet (3)

Down

1 Mona – (4)
2 Spoken (4)
3 Contributed money (10)
4 Apprehend (6)
6 Successful person (8)
7 Solitary (8)
9 Replicate (5)
12 Charge (10)
14 Sporty (8)
15 Indian cooking method (8)
18 Star sign (5)
20 Fleet of warships (6)
22 Mediterranean isle (4)
23 Dull pain (4)

67

Across

1 Seed released by plant (6)
4 Simpler (6)
7 Augment (8)
9 Cribs (7)
12 Funny (5)
13 Thoughts (5)
15 Tracks (5)
16 Occurrence (5)
17 Consumed (5)
18 Gently mock (5)
19 Taxonomic group (7)
23 Posture (8)
24 Adjourn (6)
25 Express agreement (6)

Down

1 Ethical standards (10)
2 Engine (10)
3 Practice session (8)
4 Always (4)
5 Beach constituent (4)
6 Slight advantage (4)
8 e.g. Physicist (9)
10 Written material (10)
11 Small colony (10)
14 Guards (8)
20 Yearn (4)
21 Concern (4)
22 Spikes (of cereals) (4)

68

Across

7 Grumbler (6)
8 Resale (anag.) (6)
10 (Illegal) commission (4-3)
11 English river (5)
12 Strike-breaker (4)
13 Not light (5)
17 English city (5)
18 Bounder; part of foot (4)
22 Aside (5)
23 Lawn game (7)
24 Dog (6)
25 Ten-year period (6)

Down

1 Bishop-saint (7)
2 Thieving bird (7)
3 County in South-west England (5)
4 Merry (7)
5 Wedding guide (5)
6 Mediterranean isle (5)
9 Composer of operettas (9)
14 Material (7)
15 Occurring at fixed intervals (7)
16 Bombed from above (7)
19 Contented (5)
20 Brother of... (5)
21 ...this OT prophet (5)

69

Across

1 Loop of pile fabric; England footballer (5)
4 Conservative (4)
7 True (4)
8 Arguments (8)
9 Importing illegally (9)
10 Physical education (3)
12 Irregular discoloration (6)
14 One for the pot (3,3)
16 Astern (3)
18 Landlocked anchorage in Orkney Islands (5,4)
21 Result of division sum (8)
22 African antelope (4)
23 Trad (4)
24 Portion (5)

Down

1 Rising warm air (7)
2 Demote (8)
3 Sing high (5)
4 Fruit-basket (4)
5 Shrill (5)
6 Newsgroups worldwide (6)
11 Youthful affection (4-4)
13 Ball-game (6)
15 Lace toy (anag.) (7)
17 Animal life (5)
19 Accommodate (3,2)
20 Alphabet (1,2,1)

Across

1 European language (5)
4 Indicate (5)
10 – Chaplin (7)
11 Attractive young woman (5)
12 Broom (5)
13 Neuter (7)
15 Cosy place (4)
17 David – George, PM 1916–22 (5)
19 Vitality (5)
22 Robe (4)
25 – Monroe (7)
27 Fit out (5)
29 Frozen rain (5)
30 Green gemstone (7)
31 Spirit of the air (5)
32 Later (5)

Down

2 TV police drama (1,4)
3 Slander (7)
5 At exactly the right moment (2,3)
6 Put morn (anag.); bridge call (2-5)
7 – diving (5)
8 Las – (5)
9 Aspic (5)
14 Pack away (4)
16 Irritable (4)
18 Robbery (7)
20 Feels on (anag.) (7)
21 Break (5)
23 Beginning (5)
24 Digger (5)
26 Alleviate (3,2)
28 Custom (5)

71

Across

1 Rank below baronet (6)
4 Positions (5)
8 Great (5)
9 Betrothed (7)
10 Wear (7)
11 Release (4)
12 Great expanse of water (3)
14 Kent town (4)
15 Rubber tube on a wheel (4)
18 Ogle (3)
21 A single thing (4)
23 Permitted (7)
25 Progressive (7)
26 Test (5)
27 Horror (5)
28 Threaded fasteners (6)

Down

1 Pecks (6)
2 Enhance (7)
3 Beastly (8)
4 Groan (4)
5 Big cat (5)
6 Abrupt (6)
7 Intends (5)
13 Strong and vigorous (8)
16 Transcribe again (7)
17 Sturdy and rough (6)
19 Large bird of prey (5)
20 Grown-ups (6)
22 Picture (5)
24 Finance (4)

Across

1 Set of rooms (5)
4 Satisfy (4)
8 Drug (3)
9 Spanish city (9)
10 Small furnace (4)
11 Outline of dramatic work (8)
12 Mimic (3)
13 Emotional shock (6)
14 Poem (6)
16 Star (3)
17 Custom (8)
18 Protest (4)
20 Thick-skinned animal (9)
21 Decline (3)
22 Daze (4)
23 Unit of length (5)

Down

1 Maintain (7)
2 Undecided (2,3,7)
3 Convenient (4)
4 Spite (6)
5 Capital of Alberta (8)
6 Violation (12)
7 Ring round the head (4)
11 Resort (3)
12 Type of quartz (8)
14 Take legal action (3)
15 Disturbance (7)
16 Sort out (6)
17 Tube (4)
19 Prayer leader (4)

The Telegraph

73

Across

1 Smile soppily (6)
4 Parts of legs (6)
7 Resentfully (8)
9 e.g. The Canaries (7)
12 Cog (5)
13 Regions (5)
15 Synthetic material (5)
16 Survive (5)
17 River fish (5)
18 Subject matter (5)
19 Have doubts about (7)
23 Gather together (8)
24 Squirrels away (6)
25 Makes unhappy (6)

Down

1 Drugs (illegal) (10)
2 Inert (10)
3 The symbol of the Republican Party (8)
4 Playthings (4)
5 Concept (4)
6 Cargo area of ship (4)
8 Rescue craft (9)
10 Capable of being detected (10)
11 Quality of making fine distinctions (10)
14 Pay (6,2)
20 Loosen (4)
21 Impoverished (4)
22 Bottle tops (4)

Across

1 Body of matter (4)
3 Resident of Ankara maybe (4)
9 Cube of two (5)
10 Inelegant (anag.); wild rose (9)
11 Alfred −, poet (5)
12 Extreme Arctic position (5,4)
15 Harsh sound of bird (6)
17 Flashing-light device (6)
19 Entreated (9)
21 Forges (5)
23 Breathing space (9)
24 Settle (as a bird) (5)
25 Always (4)
26 Snakes (4)

Down

1 Submissive humility (8)
2 Room exposed to sun (8)
4 Total agreement (6)
5 Most eager (7)
6 Like an eyesore (4)
7 − Redding, singer (4)
8 Twelfth of foot (4)
13 Riding attire (8)
14 Lack of life (8)
16 Internet location (7)
18 Blood-sucking fly (6)
20 Eponymous OT priest (4)
21 & 22 US Army post (4,4)

75

Across

1 Empty talk (3)
3 Artifice (5)
6 Viral illness (3)
8 Zodiacal sign (5)
9 Narcissus (7)
10 Derelict (10)
12 Deviate (3)
15 Solely (4)
17 All-night dance party (4)
18 Chew (3)
22 Great work (6,4)
25 Porridge ingredient (7)
26 Custom (5)
27 Fastener (3)
28 One from South-west USA (5)
29 Aim (3)

Down

1 Ruler (8)
2 Clambers (anag.) (8)
3 Cup (6)
4 Inoculate (6)
5 Benign (6)
6 Obscene (4)
7 Hideous (4)
11 Spike of corn (3)
13 Aircraft for use in battle (8)
14 Mattress support (8)
16 Tropical vegetable (3)
19 Natural gift (6)
20 A flowing in (6)
21 Challenge (6)
23 Ruth's husband (OT) (4)
24 Prevent (4)

Across

1 Lower (6)
4 Type of carriage (6)
7 Feelers (8)
9 Cutting tool (7)
12 Obvious (5)
13 Islamic title (5)
15 Baghdad native (5)
16 One view of object (3-2)
17 Naturists (5)
18 EU currency (5)
19 Quack medicine (7)
23 Pork snack (5,3)
24 Menace (6)
25 TV (slang) (3,3)

Down

1 Italian citizen (10)
2 Front part of book (5,5)
3 Famous scientist (8)
4 Sly look (4)
5 Immediately after (4)
6 Seaweed (4)
8 CO_2 released in mines; famed part (anag.) (5-4)
10 Type of crustacean (6,4)
11 Courtroom enclosure (7,3)
14 Scientific investigation (8)
20 Lady's fingers (4)
21 Suddenly understand (4)
22 Drug-taker (4)

77

Across

1 Cunning (3)
3 Strong (5)
6 Plus (3)
8 Intended (5)
9 Greed (7)
10 Destroy (10)
12 Owns (3)
15 Pursue (4)
17 Slender (4)
18 Obtained (3)
22 Discipline (10)
25 Obsolete (7)
26 Foreign (5)
27 Lout (3)
28 Totter (5)
29 Tint (3)

Down

1 Compassion (8)
2 Desire (8)
3 Peevish (6)
4 Impotent (6)
5 Fitness (6)
6 Dry (4)
7 Expired (4)
11 Feed (3)
13 Ashamed (8)
14 Example (8)
16 Acme (3)
19 Burrow (6)
20 Resentful (6)
21 Trounce (6)
23 Refuse (4)
24 Knife (4)

Across

1 US law officer (7)
5 Traditional knowledge (4)
7 Subsequent (5)
8 Make great efforts (6)
10 Without charge (4)
11 Private (8)
13 Easily remembered (6)
14 London station (6)
17 Social event (8)
19 Company (4)
21 Flatfish (6)
22 Inexperienced (5)
23 Funny story (4)
24 Playhouse (7)

Down

1 Wrongdoer (10)
2 Withdraw (7)
3 Fling (4)
4 Take heed (6)
5 A delphinium plant (8)
6 Black crow (5)
9 Jelly-like dessert (10)
12 English county (8)
15 Three-pronged spear (7)
16 Secret (6)
18 Bass instrument (5)
20 Man-eating giant (4)

79

Across

4 Regress (6)
5 Stitched borders (4)
7 St Winifred's School Choir sang about her (7)
10 Attributes (5)
11 Instructor (7)
12 More recent (5)
14 Shapes (7)
15 Legally acceptable (5)
16 Various (7)
20 Tracks (5)
21 Joy (7)
22 Pull hard (4)
23 Go to bed (6)

Down

1 Occurrence (5)
2 Smell (5)
3 Wishes (7)
4 Uncommon (4)
6 Sofa (6)
8 Mocks (7)
9 Charged (with crime) (7)
10 High ranking officer (7)
13 Illness (6)
14 Angling (7)
17 Consult (5)
18 Lawful (5)
19 Footwear (4)

The Telegraph

Across

- **1** Shortcoming (5)
- **5** Detected aurally (5)
- **8** Adult insect (5)
- **9** Indian state (5)
- **10** Repugnant (9)
- **11** Goon (3)
- **12** In harmony with the environment (11)
- **15** Very impressive performance (11)
- **19** Purpose (3)
- **20** English poet (4,5)
- **22** Marriage (5)
- **23** More relaible (5)
- **24** – Smith, female novelist (5)
- **25** Foe (5)

Down

- **1** Tastes (8)
- **2** Dangerous (6)
- **3** Fearful (8)
- **4** German composer (6)
- **5** Trick (4)
- **6** Overseas (6)
- **7** Sleep (rough) (4)
- **13** Revelation (8)
- **14** Class of freeholders (historical) (8)
- **16** Temporarily set aside (2,4)
- **17** Non-transparent (6)
- **18** French dramatist (6)
- **20** Musical style (4)
- **21** Bird; flying toy (4)

81

Across

1 Pub (3)
3 Rage (4)
5 Abominate (4)
8 Old enough to vote (8)
10 Ballyhoo (4)
11 Past (3)
13 – board (5)
14 Blend of blues, jazz etc. (4,5)
16 Helmsman (3)
17 Assistance (3)
19 Protuberant stomach (4,5)
21 Ethical (5)
22 Long fish (3)
24 Captured (4)
25 Sorcery (8)
26 Coarse file (4)
27 Flock of quails (4)
28 Digit (3)

Down

1 Concept (4)
2 Barricaded area (2-2)
3 Comprehensible (10)
4 Rushes (anag.) (6)
6 Uncharacteristic (8)
7 One who is visually pleasing (3,5)
9 Ice-house (5)
12 Word list (10)
14 Oriental sword (8)
15 Foolishly fond of one's wife (8)
18 Not so well (5)
20 Horsy (6)
22 Redact (4)
23 Stringed instrument (4)

Across

1 Dock (4)
5 Cavity (4)
7 Consulting room (7)
8 Prison (slang) (8)
10 Made of money (4)
12 Of a hen having just laid (4)
14 Become too large (8)
16 Illegal (8)
17 Tack (4)
18 Sidepiece of a door (4)
19 Fireproof material (8)
22 Devil (3,4)
23 Hardwood (4)
24 Orient (4)

Down

1 Witty saying (4)
2 River in France and Belgium (4)
3 Compromise (5-3)
4 Lake (4)
5 Gas (8)
6 Apiece (4)
9 Dress fabric (7)
11 Highly-seasoned sausage (7)
13 Annual publication (8)
15 Bookplate (2,6)
18 Reject lover (4)
19 Verdi opera (4)
20 Behalf (4)
21 Black powder (4)

The Telegraph

83

Across

1 Former Asian country (5)
4 Joint (5)
10 Walk heavily (7)
11 Indian dish (5)
12 Monk (5)
13 Female voice (7)
15 Start (4)
17 Routine task (5)
19 Escort (5)
22 Tranquillity (4)
25 Biscuit (7)
27 Divine messenger (5)
29 Italian island (5)
30 Foolish (7)
31 Soak (5)
32 Pleased (5)

Down

2 African ruminant (5)
3 Ancient Roman ruler (7)
5 Summarise (5)
6 Outer appearance (7)
7 Employees (5)
8 Stop (5)
9 Support for cables (5)
14 Burden (4)
16 Incidental benefit (4)
18 Lively place of entertainment (3,4)
20 Sustained energy (7)
21 Bag (5)
23 Weird (5)
24 Courage (5)
26 Nimble (5)
28 Outfit (3-2)

Across

1 Pens (6)
4 Tough (anag.) (5)
8 Party with music (5)
9 Deeds (7)
10 Apportioning (7)
11 Only or just (4)
12 Consume (3)
14 Astound (4)
15 Temporary dwellings (4)
18 Expanse of water (3)
21 Birds of prey (4)
23 Restraint (7)
25 Book (7)
26 Furious (5)
27 Exhibited (5)
28 Disregard (6)

Down

1 Most broad (6)
2 Immediate (7)
3 Feelings (8)
4 Edible seeds (4)
5 Sphere (5)
6 Partakes of (6)
7 Measure (5)
13 Fancying (8)
16 Severe wind (7)
17 Woos (6)
19 Measures of land (5)
20 Container for LP (6)
22 Rope with noose (5)
24 Relation (4)

85

Across

- **1** Acquiesce (6)
- **5** Therefore (5)
- **9** Transmission (9)
- **10** Extremity (3)
- **11** Manage (3)
- **12** Person alongside (9)
- **14** Commercial vehicle (3)
- **16** Put on (a performance) (5)
- **18** Total (3)
- **19** Flat (9)
- **21** To crew (3)
- **22** Form of water (3)
- **23** Carthorse (anag.) (9)
- **25** Brief written records (5)
- **26** Hypothesis (6)

Down

- **2** Symbol of monarchy (5)
- **3** Finishes (7)
- **4** Geological period (3)
- **5** Incubate (5)
- **6** Countries (7)
- **7** Undergoing tests (12)
- **8** A word shortened (12)
- **13** Mental picture (5)
- **15** Closest (7)
- **17** Intense; furthest away (7)
- **20** Implements (5)
- **21** Engine (5)
- **24** Crib (3)

Across

1 Ship (6)
4 Lew –, tennis player (4)
9 Covered with flagstones (5)
10 Martial art (2-5)
11 Asunder (anag.); ballet performer (7)
12 Singing group (5)
13 From which place (6)
15 Become bony (6)
18 Fad (5)
20 Archangel (7)
23 Feeling (7)
24 Clutch (5)
25 Musical instrument (4)
26 Woolly coat (6)

Down

1 Two-footed animal (5)
2 Income (7)
3 Inordinate (5)
5 Things (7)
6 The same again (5)
7 Sea inlet (5)
8 Surface excavation (6)
13 Evil (6)
14 Live together in peace (7)
16 Ape (7)
17 Severe pain (5)
19 Coral island (5)
21 Bread roll (5)
22 Regress (5)

87

Across

1 Projection on rotating cylinder (3)
3 – de vie (3)
5 Eight furlongs (4)
7 Irritate (5)
8 Blackcurrant cordial (6)
10 Leave out (4)
11 Minute photo (8)
13 Hot alcoholic drink (6)
14 Espresso (6)
17 Furnace (historic) (8)
19 Cosy (4)
21 Cream cake (6)
22 Thump (5)
23 Open-topped container (4)
24 Tiny child (3)
25 Vast age (3)

Down

1 South Asian grass (10)
2 Complaining (7)
3 Eternally (4)
4 Ragamuffin (6)
5 Fungus (8)
6 Scottish squire (5)
9 Reinforce (10)
12 Appetiser (8)
15 Public money (7)
16 Red wine (6)
18 Macho (anag.); coffee with chocolate (5)
20 Slight quarrel (4)

The Telegraph

88

Across

1 Frequently (5)
4 Tree part (4)
8 Free (7)
9 Overstimulated (5)
10 Follow (5)
11 Addictive substance (7)
13 Scooper (6)
15 Front presented (6)
17 Electrical vehicle (7)
20 Loosened (5)
22 Uneven (5)
23 Ruin (plans) (7)
24 European John (4)
25 Ship (5)

Down

1 Handy (2,3)
2 Hot relish (7,5)
3 In no place (7)
4 Bathroom feature (5)
5 Restoration (5)
6 Very trim (5,3,4)
7 War poet (6)
12 No longer available (3)
13 Planet (6)
14 Pasture (3)
16 Customarily (2,5)
18 Aquatic rodent (5)
19 Gone up (5)
21 Artist and engraver (5)

89

Across

1 Vocalist (6)
4 Decant (4)
9 Confess (5)
10 Weariness (7)
11 Fault (7)
12 Unmoving (5)
13 Dear (6)
15 Chief (6)
18 Hosiery (5)
20 Stares (7)
23 Speech (7)
24 Dispute (5)
25 Immense (4)
26 Lease (6)

Down

1 Horde (5)
2 Retribution (7)
3 Spare (5)
5 External (7)
6 Scoundrel (5)
7 Following (5)
8 Superior (6)
13 Universe (6)
14 Durable (7)
16 Pleasure (7)
17 Torment (5)
19 Train (5)
21 Lacquer (5)
22 Purloin (5)

The Telegraph

90

Across

1 Fragrant gum resin (5)
4 Marie –, chemist (5)
8 Short sleep (3)
9 Actor's make-up (11)
10 Insect (7)
12 Level (5)
13 Smile affectedly (6)
14 Antelope (6)
17 Rapid (5)
19 Merciful (7)
21 Soft cloth cap (11)
23 Anger (3)
24 Card game (5)
25 Viewpoint (5)

Down

1 Great power (5)
2 Type of whisky (3)
3 Antagonistic (7)
4 Metallic element (6)
5 Lift (5)
6 Retinue (9)
7 Hamlet character (7)
11 Residue (9)
13 Uphold (7)
15 US state (7)
16 Stylish (6)
18 Unit of heat energy (5)
20 Abrupt (5)
22 Small barrel (3)

91

Across

1 Exposed (of cover) (5)
4 Gush (6)
7 Towards the exterior (7)
8 Wreck (4)
10 Elk (5)
11 Those of the monarchy (7)
14 Goulash (4)
16 A score (6)
18 Most recent (6)
21 Overtake (4)
23 Section of book (7)
26 Lance (5)
27 Sharpen (4)
28 Windstorm (7)
29 Not moving (6)
30 Appointments (5)

Down

1 Witch's transport (10)
2 Result (7)
3 Closest (7)
4 Last out (6)
5 Cross-channel boat (5)
6 Craft; dexterity (5)
9 Strange (10)
12 Nocturnal birds (4)
13 Social insect (3)
15 Printed characters (4)
17 Short sleep (3)
19 Self-confident (7)
20 Graceful (7)
22 Of the North Pole (6)
24 Assume (5)
25 A nice surprise (5)

Across

1 Canopy over four-poster bed (6)
4 Simeon (anag.) (6)
7 Magicked (8)
9 Goddess of revenge (7)
12 Electronic communication (5)
13 Covered with climbing plant (5)
15 Speaks (5)
16 Mistake (5)
17 Do well (5)
18 Dire (5)
19 Gist (7)
23 Moves forward (8)
24 Slight movement of air (6)
25 Hot spring (6)

Down

1 Paper thrown in US celebrations (6,4)
2 Father Christmas (5,5)
3 Make the same (8)
4 Manner (4)
5 Back of neck (4)
6 Sewer's case (4)
8 Surrounded (9)
10 Things given up (10)
11 Bacteria-destroyer (10)
14 American state (8)
20 Acidic (4)
21 OT book (4)
22 Money (4)

93

Across

1 At this place (4)
5 Garden flower (4)
7 Received gladly (7)
8 Port near Dundee (8)
10 Billow (4)
12 Light fawn (4)
14 Gluing (8)
16 Restaurant (8)
17 Food (slang) (4)
18 Stronghold (4)
19 Salutation (8)
22 Hug (7)
23 In footwear (4)
24 Crush to pulp (4)

Down

1 Informal 19 across (4)
2 Jug (4)
3 Detergent (8)
4 Scottish lake (4)
5 Rouse again (8)
6 Margin (4)
9 Accept (7)
11 In ovens (anag.) (7)
13 Loosened (8)
15 Maybe (1,4,3)
18 Peck (4)
19 Pass (2,2)
20 Pour (4)
21 Pour forth (4)

Across

- **1** Whin (5)
- **4** Feature (5)
- **8** Regrettable (3)
- **9** Portable means of communication (6,5)
- **10** Repeals (anag.) (7)
- **12** Upright part of a step (5)
- **13** Group of six (6)
- **14** Prattle (6)
- **17** Drugs agent (US slang) (5)
- **19** Delighted in (7)
- **21** Drink excessively (11)
- **23** Second person (3)
- **24** Show off (5)
- **25** Electronic message (5)

Down

- **1** Thigh bone (5)
- **2** Polish (3)
- **3** Blot out (7)
- **4** Hat (6)
- **5** Love affair (5)
- **6** It spreads sleeping sickness (6,3)
- **7** Contrary (7)
- **11** Very comfortable (9)
- **13** Quick crossword clue (7)
- **15** Decide (7)
- **16** –'s swan (6)
- **18** The 24th Greek letter (5)
- **20** Reside (5)
- **22** Meadow (3)

95

Across

1 Small mark (5)
4 Spud (5)
8 Flightless bird (3)
9 Pretty (4-7)
10 Beer container (4,3)
12 Farmyard creatures (5)
13 Rudimentary state (6)
14 Bewilder (6)
17 Reliable (5)
19 One behaving without seriousness (7)
21 Knowledge (11)
23 Newspaper (3)
24 Boundary of field (5)
25 Vacant (5)

Down

1 Vista (5)
2 Conceit (3)
3 Spoilsport (7)
4 Depression (6)
5 Fastening (5)
6 Sorry (9)
7 Plain (7)
11 Racing sledge (9)
13 Trap (7)
15 Excite (7)
16 18th-century novelist (6)
18 Welsh county (5)
20 Liquid (5)
22 Mischievous child (3)

Across

1 Weasel-like animal (6)
4 See 15
7 She's not of the cloth (8)
9 Ship's captain (7)
12 Religion (5)
13 US state (5)
15, 16 & 4 'Goodness gracious
    – – – –' (pop song)
    (5,5,2,4)
16 See 15
17 Letter sign-off (5)
19 Type of saw (5)
20 Be audacious (3,2,2)
24 Bread roll (8)
25 Enamoured (2,4)
26 Not agreeing (2,4)

Down

1 Dissolving container (7,3)
2 Food for queen and larvae
    (5,5)
3 Outrage (8)
4 Pig sound (4)
5 Toss e.g. a coin (4)
6 Breed (4)
8 Continent (4)
10 Fertilised (flowers) (10)
11 Irrational (10)
14 Impede (8)
18 Arm bone (4)
21 Wet weather (4)
22 Enthusiastic about (4)
23 Woodwind instrument (4)

97

Across

1 Tennis arena (5)
4 Motionless (5)
8 Knock (3)
9 Salad dressing (11)
10 Allow (7)
12 List of charges (5)
13 Mistakes (6)
14 Mean (6)
17 Origins (5)
19 The great circle (7)
21 With pictures (11)
23 Posed (3)
24 Threads (5)
25 Stratum (5)

Down

1 Polite (5)
2 Large pot (3)
3 Slenderer (7)
4 Mediterranean country (6)
5 Enrol (5)
6 Hospital care (9)
7 Fought against (7)
11 Peculiarity (9)
13 Sincere; enthusiastic (7)
15 Having no preference (7)
16 Brutes (6)
18 Of the sun (5)
20 Additional clause (5)
22 Attempt (3)

The Telegraph

Across

1 Musical event (7)
5 Part of target (5)
8 Projection on letter (5)
9 People moving to another country (7)
10 Improve quality of (7)
11 Native of Baghdad perhaps (5)
12 Romeo's lover (6)
14 Use (6)
17 Snake (5)
19 Precursor of Crown Courts (7)
22 Desperate (7)
23 Money bag (5)
24 Brandish (5)
25 Cooperation (7)

Down

1 Social class in Hinduism (5)
2 Sea mammal (7)
3 Small and delicate (5)
4 Arranged in rows (6)
5 Metallic element (7)
6 Manor (anag.) (5)
7 In a way that involves danger (7)
12 Thieving bird (7)
13 Lifted up in praise (7)
15 Brother of Martha and Mary (NT) (7)
16 Scallywag (6)
18 Courageous (5)
20 Shade of brown (5)
21 Lustre (5)

99

Across

1 Male deer (4)
4 Worker (4)
8 Flatfish (4)
9 Neglect (9)
11 Rogue (6)
13 Accountant (7)
15 Indoor plant known as Painted Nettle (6)
16 Separate chaff from grain (6)
18 Golf club (6)
20 Consisting of more than one (6)
22 Drastic (7)
23 Annual dog show (6)
25 Day before (9)
26 Extremely (4)
27 Particle (4)
28 Seaweed (4)

Down

2 Reference line (4)
3 Rotational force; roquet (anag.) (6)
4 Scottish dish (6)
5 Slender (6)
6 Employment exchange (3,6)
7 Enthusiasm (4)
10 Dish made in mould (7)
12 Waste matter (4)
13 With equal scores (3,6)
14 Uncertainty (7)
17 Go on foot (4)
19 Protrude; exerts (anag.) (6)
20 For the time being (Latin abbrev.) (3,3)
21 Italian region (6)
23 Grotto (4)
24 Venom-tooth (4)

The Telegraph

100

Across

1 Manage (3)
3 Shared (2,6)
9 Hebridean island (5)
10 Arab state (7)
11 – Costello, Abbott's partner (3)
13 Rascal (9)
14 & 16 Ex-Poet Laureate (6,6)
18 Reach required standard (7,2)
20 Storm-centre (3)
22 Possible to be defended (7)
23 Scandinavian (5)
25 Humanitarian organisation (3,5)
26 Lunatic (3)

Down

1 Badger-like animal (5)
2 And not (3)
4 Sudan desert (6)
5 Shakespeare play (7)
6 In the interim (9)
7 Nine-sided figure (7)
8 State of disorder (4)
12 Swampy (9)
14 Measurer of current (7)
15 EU food code (1,6)
17 Break (6)
19 Light red (4)
21 Throw out (5)
24 Managed (3)

101

Across

1 Citadel (4)
3 Skips (4)
9 Simpleton (5)
10 Disgust (9)
11 Tiptoe (5)
12 Headroom (9)
15 Oration (6)
17 Belittle (6)
19 Timely (9)
21 Unspoken (5)
23 Cyclone (9)
24 Pursue (5)
25 Appear (4)
26 Encounter (4)

Down

1 Predict (8)
2 Critiqued (8)
4 East (6)
5 Earnest (7)
6 Sunny (4)
7 Halt (4)
8 Obscure (4)
13 Control (8)
14 Concern (8)
16 Raiment (7)
18 Meagre (6)
20 Bankrupt (4)
21 Diplomacy (4)
22 Gossip (4)

The Telegraph

Across

1 Slingback, e.g. (4)
4 Speed (4)
8 Conifer, e.g. (4)
9 Body of troops (9)
11 Lounge bar (6)
13 Insect; game (7)
15 – Irons, actor(6)
16 Coercion (6)
18 Sooner (6)
20 Pay tribute to (6)
22 Dumbfound (7)
23 Approach and address (6)
25 King of Kent (9)
26 Ploy (4)
27 On an occasion (4)
28 Flightless bird (4)

Down

2 Listen to (4)
3 Whole (6)
4 Insurance contract (6)
5 Shut (6)
6 Wrong (9)
7 Stingy (4)
10 Innate (7)
12 Slightly open (4)
13 Fault-finding (9)
14 Huge (7)
17 Casserole (4)
19 Corrupt (6)
20 Globe (6)
21 Sawn timber (6)
23 Indian city (4)
24 A soft cheese (4)

103

Across

1 Attempts (4)
4 Right-wingers (6)
7 Geological period (3)
9 Mark left by injury (4)
10 Biting (8)
11 Examine carefully (3)
12 Continent (4)
13 Act of democracy (8)
16 Donations (13)
19 Valedictory (8)
23 Prophet (4)
24 Chop (3)
25 Greek and Latin studies (8)
26 Cook (4)
27 Newt (3)
28 Stuffier (6)
29 Badger's burrow (4)

Down

2 At times (12)
3 Domestic help (7)
4 Discernment (5)
5 Lift (5)
6 Boat crew (5)
8 Public statement (12)
14 Tag (5)
15 Crib (3)
17 Tier (3)
18 Bugs (7)
20 Tripod (5)
21 Departs (5)
22 Optical device (5)

The Telegraph

Across

1 Grain for food (4)
5 1760 yards (4)
7 Capital of Sicily (7)
8 Soft leather shoe (8)
10 Wharf (4)
12 Member of a Bantu family (4)
14 Most ardent (8)
16 French general (2,6)
17 Noise of pig (4)
18 Portico (4)
19 Man symbolising England (4,4)
22 Swathe (7)
23 Stirling or Kate? (4)
24 Unwanted plant (4)

Down

1 Wander (4)
2 Long poem (4)
3 Very happy (8)
4 Small bird (4)
5 Insect (8)
6 Begrudge (4)
9 Luxurious (7)
11 Weaponry (7)
13 Warn Esau (anag.) (8)
15 Large mammal (8)
18 Despicable people (4)
19 Joke (4)
20 Infuse (4)
21 Noisy (4)

105

Across

1 Carried (5)
5 Plump (5)
8 Irish writer (5)
9 Film (5)
10 Snack (5,4)
11 Cloth measure (3)
12 Stormy (11)
15 Californian city (4,7)
19 Cretan mountain (3)
20 His wife could eat no lean (4,5)
22 Say (5)
23 After (5)
24 South American fox (5)
25 Sideways (3-2)

Down

1 Raised (prices) (6,2)
2 Mutiny (6)
3 Young female sheep (3-5)
4 Epidemic disease (6)
5 Words of a book (4)
6 Spanish dance (6)
7 Ship's small boat (4)
13 Cutter in (anag.) (8)
14 Cavalry unit (8)
16 Box (6)
17 Uncommonness (6)
18 Riddled (6)
20 And all that − (4)
21 Grain storage tower (4)

The Telegraph

106

Across

1 Emit smoke (4)
3 Hint (4)
9 Riddle (5)
10 The garlic (anag.) (9)
11 Convenient (5)
12 Percussion instrument (9)
15 Provoke (6)
17 Jury (Scotland) (6)
19 Go ahead of one's turn (5-4)
21 Goodbye (5)
23 Fortitude (9)
24 Standoffish (5)
25 Egg yellow (4)
26 Exclude (4)

Down

1 Resting (8)
2 Exalted (8)
4 Multitude (6)
5 Shuns (7)
6 Seabird (4)
7 Disclaim (4)
8 Slope (4)
13 Wayfaring tree (8)
14 Wife (8)
16 Dissolve (7)
18 Outdated (6)
20 Countess's husband (4)
21 Half-closed (4)
22 Flatten (4)

107

Across

1 Swift animal (4)
3 Beams of light (4)
6 Northern meadow (3)
9 Army rank (5,8)
10 A long time (8)
12 Yield (4)
13 Boy's name (Scots?) (3)
15 Rescuing (6)
18 Madman (6)
19 Children's game (3)
21 Greek love-god (4)
22 Display cabinet (8)
25 Majority 'for' vote in Parliament (3,4,4,2)
26 Furrow (3)
27 Compass point (4)
28 Boss (4)

Down

1 Fairground slide (6-7)
2 Wash in clean water (5)
4 Guinea pig-like rodent (6)
5 Vital juices (4)
6 Citizen of Middle Eastern state (7)
7 Having yellow head or tuft (birds) (6-7)
8 Long narrow flag (7)
11 US sweet potato (3)
14 Whale with tusk (7)
16 Intensely forcible (7)
17 e.g. nitrogen (3)
20 Spectres (6)
23 Watchful (5)
24 Trench (4)

26

Across

1 Route (6)
4 Nobleman's land (5)
8 Relative (5)
9 Aperture (7)
10 Various (7)
11 Sort (4)
12 Immerse (3)
14 Rang (anag.) (4)
15 Finished (4)
18 Breach (3)
21 Weapons (4)
23 Left out (7)
25 Got on (a ship) (7)
26 Perfect (5)
27 Trials (5)
28 If not (6)

Down

1 Awkward (6)
2 Expose (7)
3 Directing (8)
4 Encounter (4)
5 Loud (5)
6 Tattered (6)
7 Earth (5)
13 Place (8)
16 Outermost (7)
17 Talk at length (6)
19 Small artificial lakes (5)
20 Grown-ups (6)
22 Ways (5)
24 Totals (4)

109

Across

1 Wraith (5)
4 Value; charge (4)
8 Offer (3)
9 Welcoming (9)
10 Panache (4)
11 Opportunities (8)
12 A device used for casting metal (3)
13 Train (6)
14 Precipices (6)
16 Opponent (3)
17 Without delay (8)
18 A bare precipice (4)
20 Compliance (9)
21 A fuzzy surface texture (3)
22 Functions (4)
23 Attire (5)

Down

1 Drinking vessels (7)
2 Passé (3-9)
3 Short; tangy (4)
4 Formula (6)
5 Integral (anag.) (8)
6 Meaning (12)
7 A long time (4)
11 Lubricate (3)
12 Aquatic mammals (8)
14 Demure (3)
15 Insignia of rank (7)
16 Brief affaires (6)
17 Poke (4)
19 Bitter quarrel (4)

Across

1 Feel the absence of (4)
3 Dogs (8)
9 Reluctant prophet (5)
10 Feeling of offence (7)
11 Immature (3)
13 Orbiter of planet (9)
14 Pathos (anag.) (6)
16 Affectionate stroke (6)
18 Upstart (9)
20 Unhappy (3)
22 Code word for letter C (7)
23 Richly elegant (5)
25 Motor sport (8)
26 Undecided (4)

Down

1 Former PM (5)
2 Male scion (3)
4 Fairness (6)
5 German measles (7)
6 Testers (9)
7 (Israeli) money (7)
8 So (4)
12 Cascade (9)
14 Spirited horse (7)
15 Sausage (7)
17 At back of ship (6)
19 Republic of Ireland (4)
21 Senior member (5)
24 Hint (3)

111

Across

1 Female ruff (3)
3 For each (3)
5 Swear (slang) (4)
7 Avoids (5)
8 Rickety old car (6)
10 Skeletal (4)
11 Sickly sentimentality (8)
13 Sumptuousness (6)
14 Manet's (anag.) (6)
17 Falling (8)
19 Indigo (4)
21 Club (6)
22 Weighty (5)
23 Leg joint (4)
24 Bundle (3)
25 Light breeze (3)

Down

1 Laughter (10)
2 Vernal – (7)
3 Shove (4)
4 Discard (6)
5 Catastrophe (8)
6 Calyx segment (5)
9 Part of upper atmosphere (5,5)
12 Introduction (8)
15 North-west US state (7)
16 Influx (6)
18 Lament (5)
20 Barn (4)

Across

- **1** — doll (6)
- **4** Lined up (6)
- **7** Pasta tubes (8)
- **9** Astronomical angle (7)
- **12** Reducing expenditure sharply (5)
- **13** Gleaming (5)
- **15** Plan (5)
- **16** Right-hand page (5)
- **17** Banishment (5)
- **18** Vulgar (5)
- **19** Viceroy of Egypt (7)
- **23** Mass epic (anag.) (8)
- **24** Frequent fliers (3,3)
- **25** Of rock cavities lined with crystals (6)

Down

- **1** Small Indian fish (6,4)
- **2** Awaiting payment (10)
- **3** Water land (8)
- **4** Test of knowledge (4)
- **5** Dutch cheese (4)
- **6** Send out (4)
- **8** Fill in sea (anag.) (4,5)
- **10** Empty (10)
- **11** Type of syringe (10)
- **14** Destruction (8)
- **20** Conceal (4)
- **21** Platform (4)
- **22** Air passage (4)

113

Across

1 Naked (4)
3 Path (5)
7 Cargo (4)
8 Throwaway (10)
9 Masticate (4)
12 Murder (11)
13 Subsidy (5)
15 Task (5)
19 Magician (11)
21 Measure (4)
23 Stunning (10)
24 Minus (4)
25 Curt (5)
26 Surfeit (4)

Down

1 Unkempt (10)
2 Justify (7)
3 Oppose (6)
4 Suave (6)
5 Choose (5)
6 Aviary (4)
10 Champion (4)
11 Impregnable (10)
14 Pivot (4)
16 Browbeaten (7)
17 Gambler (6)
18 Tiny (6)
20 Minimum (5)
22 Portent (4)

Across

1 Run away (4)
3 Anger (6)
9 Narrow neck of land (7)
10 Separated (5)
11 Firearm (3)
12 Way of living (9)
13 Shrewd (6)
14 Goal (6)
16 Riddle (9)
19 Furrow (3)
21 Pinny (5)
22 Amusement park (7)
23 A red wine (6)
24 Nought (4)

Down

1 Hurl (5)
2 No longer existing (7)
4 Gratifying (5-7)
5 Gain knowledge (5)
6 Withdraw (7)
7 Rudeness (12)
8 A sparkling wine (4)
13 Ancient (7)
15 Rubbish (7)
17 Bellini opera (5)
18 Fissure (4)
20 Body's trunk (5)

115

Across

1 Poor quarter of city (6)
4 Search; type of polecat (6)
7 Set of characters (8)
9 Ungenerous (7)
12 Makes waterproof (5)
13 Apprehensions (5)
15 Endure (5)
16 A compact mass (5)
17 One commanding (5)
18 Consumed (5)
19 Burdens (7)
23 Support (a cause) (8)
24 Type of cane (6)
25 Mature persons (6)

Down

1 The pampas, for example (10)
2 Stressed (10)
3 Reassign (8)
4 Destiny (4)
5 A submerged ridge of rock (4)
6 Concludes (4)
8 Set up or found (9)
10 Inlaid rust (anag.) (10)
11 Events (10)
14 Yelled (8)
20 Nimbus (4)
21 Speechless (4)
22 Reverberate (4)

The Telegraph

116

Across

1 Given inner covering (5)
4 Response (6)
9 Book of words (7)
10 Orange from Israel (5)
11 Quality of colour (4)
12 Vest (7)
13 Tank (3)
14 Cheese (4)
16 Transient touch (4)
18 Cunning (3)
20 Slanting (7)
21 Cure (anag.); unbleached linen (4)
24 Italian island (5)
25 Lethargic people (7)
26 Boil (with anger) (6)
27 Animal trail (5)

Down

1 Nabokov female (6)
2 Ex US President (5)
3 Score of nought (4)
5 Great dancer, horse (8)
6 Talks imprecisely (7)
7 Island of Venice (6)
8 Stang (anag.) (5)
13 Conquer (8)
15 Blocking of light (7)
17 Bacterium (6)
18 Grab (5)
19 Cavalryman (6)
22 Capital of Egypt (5)
23 Troublemakers (4)

117

Across

1 Walking tour (4)
4 Be in debt (3)
6 Avoid (4)
8 Earlier (6)
9 Greatest amounts (6)
10 West Indian island (8)
11 Animal skin (4)
12 Bespoke (4,2,7)
17 Sculpture (4)
19 Calibrate (8)
22 Sty (6)
23 Soothed (6)
24 Form of music (4)
25 Shy (3)
26 Mechanical repetition (4)

Down

2 Italian motor-racing circuit (5)
3 Exalt (7)
4 Rowed (5)
5 As a group (2,5)
6 Confusion (3-2)
7 Easier (7)
10 American tramp (3)
13 Metallic oxide (7)
14 In cargo (anag.) (7)
15 Disgusting filth (7)
16 First lady (3)
18 Gemstone (5)
20 Quell (5)
21 Robbery (5)

Across

1 Minting (7)
8 Noisy quarrels (7)
9 Frill of lace (5)
10 Principal church table (4,5)
11 Science room (3)
12 Precise (5)
13 Moody (5)
14 Vacillate (5)
16 Sky-blue (5)
19 Tag (3)
20 Photographic accessory (9)
22 Spanish Costa (5)
23 Otalgia (7)
24 As a result (7)

Down

1 Wheedle (6)
2 Drink alcohol (6)
3 Uncertain (2,3,3)
4 Tagged (anag.) (6)
5 Dyke builder (4)
6 Syndicate (6)
7 Fish-hawk (6)
13 Petty quarrel (8)
14 Sailed through air (6)
15 Impotence drug (6)
16 Trinket (6)
17 Athene (anag.); a colourless gas (6)
18 Head monk's office (6)
21 Cough (4)

119

Across

- **4** Husky (6)
- **5** Swift mammal (4)
- **7** Woman engaged to be married (7)
- **9** Steal (5)
- **10** Light brown (3)
- **11** Period of time (3)
- **13** Field of influence (5)
- **15** Amazing event (7)
- **16** French sculptor (5)
- **17** Fresh (3)
- **18** Extremity (3)
- **21** Celebration (5)
- **22** Wander from subject (7)
- **23** Ineffectual person (4)
- **24** Bring into use (6)

Down

- **1** Blemish (5)
- **2** Pallid (5)
- **3** Roe of sturgeon (7)
- **4** Greet (4)
- **6** Greek mathematician (6)
- **8** Senior government ministers (7)
- **9** Extend (7)
- **12** Month (3)
- **14** Sadness (6)
- **15** Tower of a mosque (7)
- **18** Swiss mountain (5)
- **19** Comical (5)
- **20** Detect (4)

Across

1 American Indian tribe (5)
3 Miss Van Outen (6)
7 Bad dream (9)
9 Wild revelry (4)
10 Leg joint...(4)
11 ...get down on it! (5)
13 Not such a good film! (1-5)
14 Citrus fruit (5)
15 Part of armour (5)
17 Rocky fragments (6)
20 Worth (5)
21 Manhandle (4)
23 Eye greedily (4)
24 Patience (9)
25 Increase (6)
26 Diminutive person (5)

Down

1 Sacred beetle
2 One (4)
3 Girl in distress? (6)
4 Annoy (4)
5 Artist's stand (5)
6 Ring (someone) (5)
7 Hitchcock film (9)
8 Following (9)
11 Famous ballet (5)
12 River embankment (5)
16 Allowance (6)
17 Musketeers writer (5)
18 Alcoholic drink (6)
19 Correct (5)
22 Coil (4)
23 French airport (4)

121

Across

1 Funeral car (6)
5 – upon; hunts (5)
9 Criteria (9)
10 Put a limit on (3)
11 Metal-bearing mineral (3)
12 Accumulator (9)
14 Fury (3)
16 Rough drawing (5)
18 Resort (3)
19 Wavered (9)
21 Type, kind (3)
22 Geological period (3)
23 Of surpassing excellence (9)
25 Secret rendezvous (5)
26 Cleanses (6)

Down

2 Rub out (5)
3 Boiled down (7)
4 Spike (of corn) (3)
5 Tapes (anag.) (5)
6 Stimulates (7)
7 Food emporia (12)
8 Amazement (12)
13 Jumped (5)
15 Rapture (7)
17 Small fry (7)
20 Land of the Dalai Lama (5)
21 Mental picture (5)
24 Scallywag (3)

The Telegraph

Across

1 Fraction of yen (3)
3 Can (3)
5 Nasty situation (4)
7 Monsters (5)
8 Unspecified device (6)
10 Scottish reformer (4)
11 Of period when James I reigned (8)
13 Flag (6)
14 Floating wreckage (6)
17 Elated (8)
19 Pope's edict (4)
21 End (6)
22 Pass on (5)
23 Charge (4)
24 Eat greedily (3)
25 Flop (3)

Down

1 e.g. newsagent (10)
2 Jittery (7)
3 Job (4)
4 English cardinal (6)
5 H in chemistry (8)
6 Belgian city (5)
9 Out of work (10)
12 Shame (8)
15 Sleazy (7)
16 Chess piece (6)
18 Award (5)
20 Boast (4)

123

Across

1 Merriment (3)
3 Mother (3)
5 Denoted (5)
8 Most famous celebrities (1-4)
9 Help (7)
10 Contract (4)
11 Clear soup (8)
13 Ambush (6)
14 My robe (anag.) (6)
17 Mêlée (8)
19 6th Greek letter (4)
22 Squirm (7)
23 Testify (5)
24 Recover (5)
25 Evergreen tree (3)
26 Young goat (3)

Down

1 Candid (5)
2 Loudly (7)
3 Obligation (4)
4 16th- or 17th-century drama (6)
5 Virility (8)
6 Fruit of oak (5)
7 Trooped (anag.) (7)
12 Onerously (8)
13 Bereaved husband (7)
15 Male deer (7)
16 Impudent (6)
18 Broil (5)
20 Greenfly (5)
21 Make a promise (4)

Across

1 Scottish city (8)
8 Argent (6)
9 Anticipate (6)
10 Run through (8)
11 Inadvertent explosion of air (6)
13 Urgent (8)
17 Utterly lazy (4-4)
20 Wine vessel (6)
23 Tract (8)
25 Bottle to dip pen in (6)
26 End abruptly (3,3)
27 Gradient (anag.) (8)

Down

2 Poison (5)
3 Female ruff; a bailiff (5)
4 Brave (8)
5 Good sense of humour (1,1,1,1)
6 At all times (6)
7 School period (6)
11 Healing crust (4)
12 Paradise (4)
14 Optional (8)
15 Hebridean island (4)
16 Movable barrier (4)
18 Shady (6)
19 Use (6)
21 Gardened (5)
22 Glower (5)
24 Attic (4)

125

Across

1 Faults (6)
4 Legend (4)
8 Acquire (6)
9 Stylish (6)
10 Energetic (5)
11 Inebriated (7)
13 Heath (4)
15 Misery (3)
16 Soil (4)
18 Firm (7)
20 Gradient (5)
23 Negation (6)
24 Enrage (6)
25 Test (4)
26 Concurs (6)

Down

1 Ban (7)
2 Wanders (5)
3 Tirade (4)
5 Longed (7)
6 Speed (5)
7 Vamoose (7)
12 Shrink (7)
14 Facsimile (7)
17 Subjugate (7)
19 Overweight (5)
21 Shelf (5)
22 Complacent (4)

The Telegraph

Across
- **1** Boast (4)
- **3** Continent (4)
- **9** Manservant (5)
- **10** Lack of energy (9)
- **11** Arrive at (5)
- **12** Sensational play (9)
- **15** Italian painter (6)
- **17** Downpour (6)
- **19** Deny (9)
- **21** Venomous snake (5)
- **23** Unfeeling (9)
- **24** Puccini opera (5)
- **25** Repair (4)
- **26** Form of poker (4)

Down
- **1** Disaster (8)
- **2** Out-of-date (8)
- **4** Screech (6)
- **5** Mediocre (7)
- **6** Forearm bone (4)
- **7** Impatient desire (4)
- **8** Female deer (4)
- **13** Capital of Hungary (8)
- **14** Set free (8)
- **16** Biblical patriarch (7)
- **18** Wrench (6)
- **20** Oval fruit (4)
- **21** A musical (4)
- **22** Foundation (4)

127

Across

1 Plate on horse (4)
3 Respiratory infection (5)
7 Bovine animals (4)
8 Small colony (10)
9 Relaxation (4)
12 Persons (11)
13 Hibernian (5)
15 Impact (5)
19 Loggers (11)
21 Witnessed (4)
23 Places for lessons (10)
24 Using speech (4)
25 Type of duck (5)
26 Exchanged for money (4)

Down

1 Shady; untrusting (10)
2 Ledger records (7)
3 Deferred payment (6)
4 Having a function (6)
5 Overnight accommodation (5)
6 Gambles (4)
10 Earth's largest continent (4)
11 Stressed (10)
14 Not in active use (4)
16 Infers logically (7)
17 On a ship (6)
18 Rubber (6)
20 Male relative (5)
22 Merit (4)

The Telegraph

Across

1 Comes to land (7)
5 Female sorcerer (5)
8 Form of water (5)
9 Substance aiding metabolism (7)
10 Box carried on poles (9)
12 Drink; meal (3)
13 Spanish fleet (6)
14 Move unsteadily (6)
17 Vessel; impact (3)
18 Private car driver (9)
20 Obscure (7)
21 Additional (5)
23 Unpleasant (5)
24 Group of guns (7)

Down

1 Fable-teller (5)
2 Eisenhower (3)
3 Man, manlike beast (7)
4 Taste (6)
5 Teutonic god (5)
6 Schedule of events (9)
7 Poisonous plant (7)
11 Five-lined verses (9)
13 Break from meeting (7)
15 Way-out (7)
16 Croatian capital (6)
18 Like toffee (5)
19 Prepared (5)
22 Neckpiece (3)

129

Across

1 Cat sound (4)
4 Hebridean island (4)
8 Tardy (4)
9 Pervaded (9)
11 Run lad (anag.), dull person (6)
13 Registration paper (7)
15 Jinx (6)
16 More rainy (6)
18 Purifier (6)
20 Mocha (6)
22 Hit term (anag.), it's used in welding (7)
23 Keeper (6)
25 Vegetable (9)
26 Trickle slowly (4)
27 Ait (4)
28 Exude (4)

Down

2 Second-hand (4)
3 Martinet (6)
4 Rhyming game (6)
5 Keep hidden (3,3)
6 Garden flower (9)
7 Bracken (4)
10 Duchy (7)
12 Cook (4)
13 Sideless wagon (3-6)
14 Garden flower (7)
17 Marsh grass (4)
19 Macaque (6)
20 Fold (6)
21 Mozart's 'Marriage' (6)
23 Wow! (4)
24 Hum (4)

Across

1 Burrowing animal (6)
5 Moneyless (5)
9 Mine host (9)
10 Chopper (3)
11 Swim (3)
12 Remarkable tale (4,5)
14 Sprite (3)
16 European capital (5)
18 Star sign (3)
19 US state (9)
21 On holiday (3)
22 Food container (3)
23 Patience (9)
25 Snatch (5)
26 Employee (6)

Down

2 Confess (3,2)
3 Shoe-layer material; dregs in glass (7)
4 Tear (3)
5 Scots poet (5)
6 Enjoying luck (2,1,4)
7 Now and again (5,2,5)
8 Blast! (12)
13 London sports ground (5)
15 Supply funds (7)
17 Jersey (7)
20 Picture stand (5)
21 Postponed (2,3)
24 Down (3)

131

Across

1 Run away (4)
5 Former Prime Minister (4)
7 Malign (7)
8 Clue (8)
10 Move very slowly (4)
12 Petty quarrel (4)
14 Cherish (8)
16 Game for one (8)
17 Departure (4)
18 Profound (4)
19 Leguminous plant (8)
22 Forbear (7)
23 Nervous (4)
24 Slope (4)

Down

1 Commotion (4)
2 School (4)
3 French emperor (8)
4 Fair (4)
5 Descent (8)
6 Rubbish (4)
9 Copy (7)
11 Brief (7)
13 Trifles (8)
15 Irish dramatist (8)
18 Seedy bar (4)
19 Small restaurant (4)
20 County (4)
21 Female relative (4)

132

Across

1 Chess piece (6)
4 Fragrant herb (5)
8 Seal (5)
9 Coped with (7)
10 Clear (7)
11 Employs (4)
12 Tree (3)
14 Pool or lake (4)
15 Faculty for detecting (4)
18 Relation (3)
21 Gown of office (4)
23 American animal (7)
25 Progressive (7)
26 Picture (5)
27 Requires (5)
28 Geared (anag.) (6)

Down

1 Pecks (6)
2 Conceive (7)
3 Occurred (8)
4 Quality of sound (4)
5 Parts of eggs (5)
6 Of greatest age (6)
7 Snap (5)
13 Tapping (8)
16 Available space for keeping things (7)
17 Mythical monster (6)
19 Bore (5)
20 Mean (6)
22 Courageous (5)
24 Unopened flowers (4)

The Telegraph

133

Across

1 Looks searchingly (5)
4 Signs of sadness (5)
10 Annoyed; shook (7)
11 Clearing in wood (5)
12 Theatre play (5)
13 Foes (7)
15 Aspect (4)
17 Flax fabric (5)
19 Holy being (5)
22 Ripped (4)
25 Wrap around (7)
27 Keen (5)
29 Behaved (5)
30 Assuage (7)
31 Bordered (5)
32 Redacts (5)

Down

2 Surplus (5)
3 Free (7)
5 Two under par (5)
6 Convert into cash (7)
7 Unrefined (5)
8 Contributed (5)
9 Nous (5)
14 Approach (4)
16 Enthusiastic about (4)
18 Asked to visit (7)
20 Goaded (7)
21 Unwind (5)
23 Form of theatre (5)
24 Carrying weapons (5)
26 Masonic club (5)
28 Visitor (5)

The Telegraph

Across

1. Changes (6)
4. Unlike flat land (5)
8. Striped animal (5)
9. Eight-sided figure (7)
10. Interlace (7)
11. Irish language (4)
12. Bark constantly (3)
14. Skin condition (4)
15. Solemn promise (4)
18. Fairy-like creature (3)
21. Wealthy (4)
23. Even-tempered (7)
25. Chinese capital (7)
26. Got up (5)
27. Wooden shoe (5)
28. Repaired (6)

Down

1. Muslim minister (6)
2. Mechanical (7)
3. Person being tested (8)
4. Loathe (4)
5. Type of beer (5)
6. American (loosely) (6)
7. Cash (5)
13. The people (8)
16. Type of newspaper (7)
17. Greek god of darkness (6)
19. Pretend (5)
20. Virgil's epic (6)
22. Go up (5)
24. Tartan skirt (4)

135

Across

1 Fresh (3)
3 Unclouded (5)
6 Female sandpiper (3)
8 Stage-player (5)
9 Skyline (7)
10 Young friend (10)
12 Tibetan ox (3)
15 Upper covering (4)
17 Seabird (4)
18 Interval (3)
22 An earlier issue (4,6)
25 Eye specialist (7)
26 Tartan (5)
27 Sly person (3)
28 Pierced (5)
29 Excavated (3)

Down

1 Biblical boat (5,3)
2 Guardian (8)
3 Ribbon (6)
4 Disinter (6)
5 Unusual item (6)
6 Destroy completely (4)
7 Volcano in Sicily (4)
11 Devour (3)
13 Part of piano (8)
14 Unbecoming (5,3)
16 Excellent (slang) (3)
19 Covering with slabs (6)
20 Streak (anag.) (6)
21 Leapt (6)
23 Suffered defeat (4)
24 Pound (4)

Across

1 Fellow (3)
3 Scottish river (3)
5 Conscious existence (4)
8 Small ships (5)
9 Settlement (7)
10 Set of three (7)
12 Irish celebrity (5)
13 Flooded valley (3)
15 Muddy (5)
17 Garment (3)
19 – Street-Porter (5)
20 Egyptian monument (7)
23 Haven (7)
24 Pile fabric (5)
25 Wife of Jacob (OT) (4)
26 Plus (3)
27 Rose fruit (3)

Down

1 Gang member (7)
2 Canteen (5)
3 Dance club (5)
4 Void (5)
5 Set aside (3,4)
6 Fighter (anag.) (7)
7 Famous school (4)
11 Sentimentality (3)
14 Racecourse (7)
15 Promise to marry (7)
16 Effigy (3)
18 Hurry along (5-2)
19 Gospel writer (4)
20 Windcheater (5)
21 Regarded (5)
22 Swamp (5)

137

Across

1 Wages (3)
3 Roost (5)
6 Expert (3)
8 Distribute (5)
9 Spliced (7)
10 Quench (10)
12 Blubber (3)
15 Loosen (4)
17 Spout (4)
18 Moose (3)
22 Tiny (10)
25 Sentimental (7)
26 Hail (5)
27 Belly (3)
28 Comeback (5)
29 Star (3)

Down

1 Amicable (8)
2 Christmas (8)
3 Intoxicating (6)
4 Hearsay (6)
5 Badger (6)
6 Dry (4)
7 Whirlpool (4)
11 Porker (3)
13 Commerce (8)
14 Menace (8)
16 Aged (3)
19 Executioner (6)
20 Abduct (6)
21 Ravenous (6)
23 Complacent (4)
24 Bosom (4)

Across

1 Fuse (4)
4 Relax (4)
8 Male deer (4)
9 Very funny (9)
11 Courageous (6)
13 Clique (7)
15 Grumbled (6)
16 Tyrant (6)
18 French port (6)
20 Antenna (6)
22 Back (7)
23 Sturdy (6)
25 Restaurant (9)
26 Planet (4)
27 Expensive (4)
28 Steal (4)

Down

2 Wicked (4)
3 Monster (6)
4 Lifted (6)
5 Foolish (6)
6 Store up (9)
7 Unattractive (4)
10 Inactive spy (7)
12 Surrounded by (4)
13 A French cheese (9)
14 Windy storm (7)
17 Conservative (4)
19 Meal course (6)
20 Promote (6)
21 Paid companion (6)
23 Capital of Italy (4)
24 Choose (4)

139

Across

1 Temporary inactivity (5)
4 Entire (5)
10 Function (7)
11 Miserly; drunk (5)
12 Praise highly (5)
13 Criminal (7)
15 Always (4)
17 Musical drama (5)
19 Frequently (5)
22 Quality of a voice (4)
25 State objection (7)
27 Higher than (5)
29 Lubricated (5)
30 Belongings (7)
31 Clever (5)
32 Frighten (5)

Down

2 Main artery (5)
3 Lower in stature (7)
5 Inn (5)
6 Cases (7)
7 Hasten (5)
8 Dish out (5)
9 Peeved (5)
14 Metallic element (4)
16 Large casks (4)
18 Poser (7)
20 Apprehensive (7)
21 Dining utensil (5)
23 Different (5)
24 Minimum (5)
26 Layman of church (5)
28 Happen (5)

Across

1 Pretentious art (6)
4 Female birds (4)
8 For the time being (3,3)
9 Dog (childish) (3-3)
10 Rascal (5)
11 Moving across territories (7)
13 Pacific island state (4)
15 Pig (3)
16 Carbonated drink (4)
18 & 20 Above reproach (7,5)
23 Pleasure boat (6)
24 Flowering shrub (6)
25 Rip (4)
26 Summary (6)

Down

1 City in Pakistan (7)
2 Emblem on pole? (5)
3 Search thoroughly (4)
5 Jonathan –, triple jumper (7)
6 Faint (5)
7 Shorten (7)
12 Russian dramatist (7)
14 Flower arranging (7)
17 Most beloved (7)
19 Pursuit (5)
21 Letting contract (5)
22 Cab (4)

141

Across

1 Heir (3)
3 Bewilder (4)
5 Chill (4)
8 Former lover (3,5)
10 Unison (abbrev.) (4)
11 Draw (3)
13 Resin (anag.) (5)
14 Of debts, settled (3,6)
16 Welsh river (3)
17 Rubber tree (3)
19 Said (9)
21 Relating to a town (5)
22 Wine vintage (3)
24 After that (4)
25 Looking for (8)
26 Peer (4)
27 Aquatic bird (4)
28 Cathedral (3)

Down

1 Smut (4)
2 Unclothed (4)
3 Young offender (10)
4 Southern African country (6)
6 Greek hero (8)
7 Declines (anag.) (8)
9 Cotton yarn (5)
12 Avoidance (10)
14 Regulated (8)
15 Spinning ball (cricket) (3,5)
18 Be educated (5)
20 Tribal conference (6)
22 Quote (4)
23 Unattractive (4)

26

Across

1 Instant (5)
4 Pierce (4)
8 Spanish title (3)
9 Subjection (9)
10 Sauce base (4)
11 Marital (8)
12 Female pig (3)
13 Footman (6)
14 Place of refuge (6)
16 Spasm (3)
17 Curt poem (anag.) (8)
18 Red gemstone (4)
20 Riddle (9)
21 Menagerie (3)
22 Sobbed (4)
23 Dig (5)

Down

1 In alliance (7)
2 Declaration (12)
3 Resort adjoining Brighton (4)
4 Industrial action (2-4)
5 Set again (8)
6 Variety of beet (6-6)
7 Ringer (4)
11 Shy (3)
12 Series (8)
14 Ventilate (3)
15 It is danced round (7)
16 Polecat (6)
17 Hen's partner (4)
19 Among (4)

143

Across

1 Narrow passage (5)
4 Spat (6)
9 Grassy plain (7)
10 Mix (5)
11 Gang (4)
12 Item (7)
13 Deceive (3)
14 Examination (4)
16 Candid (4)
18 Nail (3)
20 Show lively interest (7)
21 Continent (4)
24 Indian capital (5)
25 Vigorous campaign (7)
26 Crude (6)
27 Male voice (5)

Down

1 Outlook (6)
2 Depart (5)
3 Royal house (4)
5 Goal (8)
6 Golden syrup (7)
7 Steering device (6)
8 Unbend (5)
13 Prosper (8)
15 Snake (7)
17 Interfere (6)
18 Freshwater fish (5)
19 Profession (6)
22 Blemish (5)
23 Abrupt (4)

Across

1 Mistake (5)
4 Bloodsucking mite (4)
8 Faucet (3)
9 Vision tiredness (9)
10 In a frenzy (4)
11 Horse (8)
12 Trifle (3)
13 Large bird (6)
14 Advantageous (6)
16 Skill (3)
17 Pacific island (8)
18 Swindle (4)
20 Ending (9)
21 Charged particle (3)
22 Lazy (4)
23 Tips (5)

Down

1 Draw out by force (7)
2 A copy (12)
3 Rush (4)
4 Score (6)
5 Influence for change (8)
6 Gratification (12)
7 Soon (4)
11 Male child (3)
12 Tropical tree (8)
14 Vase (3)
15 Mourns (7)
16 Reach (6)
17 Fuel from bog (4)
19 0.08333 of a foot (4)

145

Across

1 Compel (5)
4 Elevation (6)
7 Prattle (7)
8 Obligation (4)
10 Grant freedom to (5)
11 Made possible (7)
14 Long shaggy hair (4)
16 Proved (6)
18 Snow vehicle (6)
21 Engagement (4)
23 Storm (7)
26 Cleave (5)
27 Canine (4)
28 No heart (anag.) (7)
29 Series of events (6)
30 Dips (5)

Down

1 Make easier (10)
2 Logically deduces (7)
3 Utmost (7)
4 Steel oneself (6)
5 Asian republic (5)
6 Inn (5)
9 Exciting exploits (10)
12 A set (of tables) (4)
13 An extra (3)
15 Appends (4)
17 Crown (3)
19 Units of instruction (7)
20 Relative of whale (7)
22 Onslaught (6)
24 Intended (5)
25 Bird of prey (5)

Across

1 Covering one sheet of newspaper (4-4)
5 Woodworker's tool (4)
8 Mercenary worker (8)
9 Oxford's second crew (4)
11 Bellringing (11)
14 Total (3)
16 Grab (5)
17 Golfer; elevated railways (3)
18 Modifications (11)
21 Covering of tree (4)
22 Shout of praise (8)
24 Tragic king (4)
25 Easily carried (8)

Down

1 Warm, dry wind (4)
2 Song's text (5)
3 Simple taps (anag.); a manuscript (10)
4 Weapon (3)
6 Arrange (7)
7 Composition writer (8)
10 Body of rulers (10)
12 Self-evident proposition (5)
13 Turkish city (8)
15 Holiday island (7)
19 Firework (5)
20 Grow smaller (as moon) (4)
23 Constellation (3)

147

Across

1 Ascertained heaviness (7)
8 Card game (6)
9 Train enthusiast (7)
11 Comfort station (4,4)
12 Normal (5)
14 Nurse (4)
15 County in South-west England (8)
17 Elevated (8)
18 Banking system (4)
20 Cured pork (5)
21 8 across carrying water (8)
23 Slacken gradually (4,3)
24 Greek islander (6)
25 Body of serfs (7)

Down

2 Disclose (6)
3 Swiss ski resort (6)
4 Pitcher (4)
5 Ring tag (anag.) (7)
6 Expressed in distinctive or metaphorical way (9)
7 Bright scarlet (9)
10 Fragrance (9)
12 Expression in speech (9)
13 Rude injun (anag.) (9)
16 Former capital of Ivory Coast (7)
18 Summerhouse (6)
19 Thatcher e.g. (6)
22 Receive (4)

Across

1 Father (NT) (4)
3 A joint (5)
7 Accompanying (4)
8 Place of worship (10)
9 Again (4)
12 Compromise (4,3,4)
13 Slightly drunk (5)
15 Two-masted vessel (5)
19 Handcart (11)
21 Mystic symbol (4)
23 For use on land and in water (10)
24 Seaweed jelly (4)
25 Triad (5)
26 Optimistic (4)

Down

1 Completely (10)
2 Sea-legs (anag.) (7)
3 Of the moon, decreasing (6)
4 Instigate (6)
5 Twitch (5)
6 Eyelid inflammation (4)
10 Subsequent (4)
11 Diluted (5-5)
14 Chessman (4)
16 Previous (7)
17 Rage (6)
18 Constrain (6)
20 Earth (anag.) (5)
22 Press forward (4)

149

Across

1 Entwine (4)
4 Flushed (3)
6 Injure (4)
8 Chum (6)
9 Tension (6)
10 Thoroughbred (8)
11 Flush (4)
12 Forecast (13)
17 Barely (4)
19 Atrocious (8)
22 Pictures (6)
23 Unkempt (6)
24 Witticism (4)
25 Judge (3)
26 Every (4)

Down

2 Sister (5)
3 Alive (7)
4 Equestrian (5)
5 Ancestry (7)
6 Multitude (5)
7 Venerate (7)
10 Whelp (3)
13 Humdrum (7)
14 Pariah (7)
15 Atmosphere (7)
16 Ogle (3)
18 Chirp (5)
20 Hazardous (5)
21 Reason (5)

Across

1 Pace of a horse (6)
5 Coil (4)
8 Festive occasion (4)
9 Disaster (8)
10 Clergyman (6)
11 Small chicken (6)
12 Farming (11)
15 Persecute (6)
17 Formal discussion (6)
19 Type of painting (8)
20 Enthusiastic (4)
21 Expensive (4)
22 Conundrum (6)

Down

2 Violin maker (5)
3 Educator (7)
4 Sum up (5)
5 Citrus fruit (5)
6 Indignation (7)
7 Worldwide (6)
12 Edible mollusc (7)
13 Offhand (6)
14 Scold (7)
16 Change (5)
17 Discourage (5)
18 Court case (5)

Solutions

Solutions 1-2

1

Across:
1 Castor
5 Weigh (Castaway)
9 Resonance
10 Par
11 Din
12 Runners-up
14 Map
16 Log in
18 Ear
19 Navigates
21 Ash
22 Tot
23 Athletics
25 Salad
26 Engine

Down:
2 Arson
3 Tendril
4 Ran
5 Where
6 Impasse
7 Hire-purchase
8 Predominates
13 Night
15 Pivotal
17 Nest egg
20 Grand
21 Alien
24 Hoe

2

Across:
1 Maidens
5 Peach (Maiden speech)
8 Tibia
9 Ustinov
10 Embroil
11 Fixer
12 Hudson
14 Glowed
17 Blaze
19 Umpires
22 Turning
23 Alien
24 Tasty
25 Speaker

Down:
1 Metre
2 Imbibed
3 Erato
4 Squall
5 Pitiful
6 Annex
7 Hovered
12 Habitat
13 Obesity
15 Warwick
16 Judges
18 Arras
20 Phase
21 Senor

Solutions 3-4

3

4

Solutions 5-6

5

Across:
1 *Bait*
4 *Oaf*
6 *Urn* (Beethoven)
8 Substitution
10 Spoils
12 Paunch
13 Equal
14 Erse
15 Fall
17 Magic
19 Deceit
21 Chosen
23 Needleworker
24 Yap
25 Dry
26 Seep

Down:
2 Aqueous
3 Tussle
4 Omit
5 Frugal
6 Union
7 Nonchalant
9 Ascendancy
11 Squat
12 Panic
16 Austere
17 Misled
18 Chorus
20 Creep
22 Sway

6

Across:
1 Storey
4 Bored (Storyboard)
8 Rifle
9 Zealous
10 Chapter
11 Gala
12 Elk
14 Edda
15 Echo
18 Log
21 Exam
23 Avocado
25 Unicorn
26 Extra
27 Needy
28 Keynes

Down:
1 Strict
2 Offhand
3 Eventual
4 Beak
5 Rioja
6 Dismal
7 Azure
13 Kerosene
16 Hearten
17 Sequin
19 Gaunt
20 Morass
22 Agile
24 Copy

Solutions 7-8

7

Across:
1 Note
3 Acres (No takers)
7 Thor
8 Unbearable
9 Ream
12 Incompetent
13 Honed
15 Usher
19 Agoraphobia
21 Gory
23 Phlegmatic
24 Rugs
25 Yacht
26 Edgy

Down:
1 Nourishing
2 Eyesore
3 Abrupt
4 Rebate
5 Stern
6 Coma
10 Etch
11 Matriarchy
14 Near
16 Storage
17 Frolic
18 Spigot
20 Gypsy
22 Onus

8

Across:
1 *Exe*
3 *Cur*
5 *Shun* (Excursion)
7 Blank
8 Zounds
10 Oath
11 Prophecy
13 Deceit
14 Potash
17 Ravenous
19 Jung
21 Steppe
22 Miner
23 Flag
24 Sin
25 SOS

Down:
1 Embroidery
2 Elastic
3 Coke
4 Razors
5 Sculptor
6 Undue
9 Pythagoras
12 Winnipeg
15 Aquinas
16 Duress
18 Vital
20 Omen

Solutions 9–10

9

Across:
1 *Roux*
4 *Bee*
6 *Con* (Rubicon)
8 Overexposure
10 Hornet
12 Heated
13 Sadat
14 Whet
15 Prow
17 Cross
19 Heyday
21 Herbal
23 Feel the pinch
24 Tod
25 Nut
26 Tune

Down:
2 Obverse
3 Xerxes
4 Boxy
5 Exocet
6 Crust
7 Ne'er-do-well
9 Chew the fat
11 Tarry
12 Harsh
16 Rubicon
17 Caxton
18 Sexist
20 Yield
22 Text

10

Across:
1 *Ante*
3 *Cyclonic*
9 *Gloom* (Anticyclonic gloom)
10 Mixture
11 Low
13 Truncheon
14 Radius
16 United
18 Up-and-down
20 Dew
22 Dead-end
23 Facet
25 Pressure
26 High

Down:
1 Angel
2 Two
4 Yum-yum
5 Lexicon
6 Nauseated
7 Cleaned
8 Smut
12 Wide awake
14 Round up
15 Undress
17 Wonder
19 Naff
21 Witch
24 Chi

Solutions 11–12

11

Across:
1 Wilde
4 Bore (Wild boar)
8 Languid
9 Grave
10 Sword
11 Elevate
13 Centre
15 Dreary
17 Othello
20 Swarm
22 Scrap
23 Tornado
24 Zero
25 Evade

Down:
1 Wales
2 Lincolnshire
3 Ecuador
4 Badge
5 Rogue
6 Taramasalata
7 Celery
12 Led
13 Choose
14 Eel
16 Reserve
18 Lapse
19 Outdo
21 Moose

12

Across:
1 Heir
4 Weigh (Airway)
8 Solitude
9 Perk
10 I-spy
11 Apparent
12 Aplomb
14 Mellow
16 Decorous
19 Flan
20 Kiss
21 Cribbage
22 Tamar
23 Fret

Down:
2 Emily
3 Rhubarb
4 Whelp
5 Imperil
6 Heron
7 Gossip
13 Opossum
14 Mastiff
15 Orange
17 Evict
18 Oscar
19 Fable

Solutions 13–14

13

Across:
1 Weld
4 Rest (Well dressed)
8 Cure
9 Marmalade
11 Dynamo
13 Prattle
15 Hassle
16 Escort
18 Stuart
20 Orator
22 Magnets
23 Grovel
25 Decadence
26 Styx
27 Stud
28 Tart

Down:
2 Elan
3 Demurs
4 Relate
5 Saddle
6 Runabouts
7 Veto
10 Eyesore
12 Thus
13 Pseudonym
14 Alarmed
17 Turf
19 Talent
20 Onward
21 Attest
23 Gust
24 Scar

14

Across:
1 Kitsch
4 Henna (Kitchener)
8 Rogue
9 Luddite
10 Theorem
11 Shed
12 Era
14 Esau
15 Dear
18 Low
21 Asps
23 Require
25 Isobars
26 Acute
27 Crypt
28 Method

Down:
1 Karate
2 Tigress
3 Cheerful
4 Hadj
5 Neigh
6 Agenda
7 Blame
13 Adequate
16 Azimuth
17 Maniac
19 Wrist
20 Defend
22 Proxy
24 Vast

Solutions 15–16

15

Across:
1 *Dis*
3 *Function*
9 *Alley* (Dysfunctionally)
10 Foxtrot
11 Lav
13 Thin on top
14 Jigsaw
16 Abated
18 Intestate
20 Dud
22 Tabloid
23 Sabre
25 Yielding
26 Yam

Down:
1 Drawl
2 Sol
4 Unfair
5 Coxcomb
6 Irritated
7 Note-pad
8 Eyot
12 Vegetable
14 Jointly
15 Abscond
17 Madden
19 Easy
21 Dream
24 Boy

16

Across:
1 *Sell*
4 *Airy*
8 *Hack* (Celeriac)
9 Jampacked
11 Kowtow
13 Forever
15 Helper
16 Do down
18 Give up
20 Thread
22 Essayed
23 Cruise
25 Turbulent
26 Suez
27 Goat
28 Yoga

Down:
2 Exam
3 Laptop
4 Archer
5 Reeked
6 Cautioned
7 Skew
10 Dorothy
12 Shag
13 Flavoured
14 Request
17 Nude
19 Pseudo
20 Talbot
21 Really
23 Cash
24 Snag

The Telegraph

Solutions 17–18

17

Across:
1 Hardens
5 Hole (Heart and soul)
7 Loser
8 Assist
10 Chew
11 Comedown
13 Potent
14 Simple
17 Exercise
19 Knot
21 Stroll
22 Lingo
23 Rage
24 Madness

Down:
1 Helicopter
2 Respect
3 Earn
4 Season
5 Hysteria
6 Lasso
9 Infectious
12 Anecdote
15 Penance
16 Asylum
18 Extra
20 Glad

18

Across:
1 Bares
4 Write (Bears right)
10 Pursuit
11 Pipes
12 Canal
13 Reduced
15 Lung
17 Greys
19 Girls
22 East
25 Demands
27 Actor
29 Lever
30 Existed
31 Added
32 Asked

Down:
2 Apron
3 Equally
5 Rapid
6 Typical
7 Space
8 Stern
9 Aside
14 Eggs
16 Used
18 Removed
20 Italics
21 Oddly
23 Ashes
24 Trade
26 Nerve
28 Title

Solutions 19–20

Across:
1 Soles
4 Urchin (Soul searching)
7 General
8 Atom
10 Extra
11 Satisfy
14 Mess
16 Tossed
18 Ignore
21 Gear
23 Omitted
26 Alter
27 Lava
28 Trumpet
29 Temper
30 Loser

Down:
1 Suggestion
2 Lengths
3 Surname
4 Unless
5 Craft
6 Irons
9 Typewriter
12 Asia
13 Inn
15 Edge
17 Sit
19 Gradual
20 Octopus
22 Editor
24 Image
25 Tramp

19

Across:
1 Tack
4 Titian (Tactician)
7 Née
9 Shoo
10 Squabble
11 Wit
12 Yeti
13 Superior
16 Geiger counter
19 Jeweller
23 Racy
24 Err
25 Stockade
26 Oink
27 Vow
28 Sleeve
29 Suez

Down:
2 Achievements
3 Knowing
4 Tests
5 Thump
6 Amber
8 Fluorescence
14 Uncle
15 Emu
17 Ell
18 Narrows
20 Excel
21 Lease
22 Reeve

20

Solutions 21–22

21

Across:
1 **Scent**
8 Emmental (Sentimental)
9 Justice
10 Lanceted
11 Vinegar
12 Quart
15 Hewer
18 Preen
19 Radio
22 Reroute
23 Pit viper
24 Tobacco
25 Overlord
26 Steer

Down:
2 Crucifer
3 Nattered
4 Smear
5 Ketchup
6 Stature
7 Slide
8 Eclat
13 Arrogant
14 Tentacle
16 Waltzer
17 Risible
20 Herod
21 Spoon
22 Retry

22

Across:
7 Take in
8 Plaice (Taking place)
9 Burden of proof
10 Souvlaki
12 Nose
13 Scar
15 Megastar
17 Take the plunge
19 Chilli
20 Morass

Down:
1 Caruso
2 Head over heels
3 Anon
4 Spiffing
5 Fair-and-square
6 Across
11 Armchair
14 Cha-cha
16 August
18 Pump

Solutions 23–24

23

Across:
1 *War*
3 *Turf*
5 *Earn* (Water fern)
8 Instruct
10 Plum
11 Tap
13 Organ
14 Cafeteria
16 Ale
17 Rat
19 Lifestyle
21 Carol
22 Fee
24 Tier
25 Tolerant
26 Apse
27 Iris
28 Gun

Down:
1 Wait
2 Rasp
3 Tarantella
4 Rector
6 Allegory
7 Nominate
9 Naval
12 Coarseness
14 Calcutta
15 Fearless
18 Alien
20 Favour
22 Fang
23 Eton

24

Across:
1 Miss
5 Reed (Misread)
7 Elevate
8 Decrepit
10 Oust
12 Zinc
14 Esoteric
16 Pick-me-up
17 Yoke
18 Mesh
19 Tangiers
22 Laconic
23 Kite
24 Host

Down:
1 Mood
2 Sear
3 Bel paese
4 Vast
5 Recovery
6 Daft
9 Edifice
11 Sticker
13 Cake hole
15 Opponent
18 Mock
19 Tact
20 Itch
21 Slit

The Telegraph

Solutions 25–26

25

Across:
1 Reverse
5 Hide (Riverside)
7 Apron
8 Rested
10 Omit
11 Chairman
13 Awhile
14 Barrel
17 Listened
19 Data
21 Cabins
22 China
23 Plug
24 Suspect

Down:
1 Reasonable
2 Varnish
3 Rank
4 Earths
5 Hospital
6 Dream
9 Unpleasant
12 Sleeping
15 Realise
16 Ceases
18 Stall
20 Ices

26

Across:
1 Manned
4 Aits (Mandates)
9 Drawn
10 Portico
11 Examine
12 Adept
13 Shabby
15 Ashram
18 Bijou
20 Vandyke
23 Languid
24 Craft
25 Hate
26 Tendon

Down:
1 Midge
2 Niagara
3 Ennui
5 Inroads
6 Seize
7 Speed
8 Tom-tom
13 Subtle
14 Bouquet
16 Reynard
17 Evade
19 Jonah
21 Niche
22 Eat in

Solutions 27–28

27

28

The Telegraph

Solutions 29–30

29

Across:
7 Injure
8 Notion (Indian Ocean)
10 License
11 Spire
12 Keep
13 Leper
17 False
18 Warp
22 Clear
23 Trailer
24 Amulet
25 Uranus

Down:
1 Dislike
2 Ejected
3 Brand
4 Monster
5 Rigid
6 Angel
9 Necessity
14 Married
15 Garland
16 Oppress
19 Scram
20 Jesus
21 Fairy

30

Across:
1 Summer
5 Salts (Somersaults)
9 Lemon peel
10 Och
11 Can
12 Cock-a-hoop
14 Air
16 Twerp
18 Ton
19 De rigueur
21 Sea
22 Lad
23 Oast house
25 Epsom
26 Middle

Down:
2 Unman
3 Manx cat
4 Roe
5 Salsa
6 Lookout
7 Schopenhauer
8 Black and blue
13 Crete
15 Reredos
17 Parched
20 Groom
21 Skull
24 Sum

Solutions 31–32

31

32

Solutions 33–34

33

Across:
1 Backed
4 Eerier (Bacteria)
9 Ology
10 Uniform
11 Pub
12 Upset
13 Brioche
15 Evaporating
19 Marxist
20 Jaunt
21 Aha
22 Legroom
24 Zoril
25 Modify
26 Hybrid

Down:
1 Blow up
2 Cross over
3 Egypt
5 Elitist
6 I do
7 Ramsey
8 Rubber-stamp
14 Conqueror
16 Pair off
17 Emblem
18 Stolid
20 Jazzy
23 God

34

Across:
1 *Back*
4 *Tier*
8 *Rear* (Bacteria!)
9 Fortnight
11 Artery
13 Bacilli
15 Viagra
16 Evilly
18 Modest
20 Patron
22 Trolley
23 Gateau
25 Larcenous
26 Ring
27 Stud
28 Size

Down:
2 Avow
3 Kitbag
4 Tricia
5 Exhale
6 Jewellery
7 Dray
10 Trivial
12 Ovum
13 Bandstand
14 Crystal
17 Yank
19 Truant
20 Placid
21 Tennis
23 Germ
24 Quiz

Solutions 35-36

Across:

1   Ceiling
8   Whacks (Sealing wax)
9   Itemise
11 Tranquil
12 Irene
14 Meat
15 Poseidon
17 Attorney
18 Lead
20 False
21 Spacious
23 Shatter
24 Videos
25 Respite

Down:

2   Entire
3   Lament
4   Nest
5   Channel
6   Scoundrel
7   Esplanade
10 Erroneous
12 Impassive
13 Eastwards
16 Traitor
18 Laptop
19 Assent
22 Shoe

35

Across:

1   Quire
4   Buoy (Choirboy)
8   Illness
9   Thorn
10 Organ
11 Sincere
13 Retort
15 Elicit
17 Combine
20 Aloof
22 Title
23 Snippet
24 Stem
25 Girth

Down:

1   Quito
2   Illegitimate
3   Eleanor
4   Basis
5   Often
6   Come a cropper
7   Invent
12 Ice
13 Recite
14 Tan
16 Leaning
18 Inert
19 Epsom
21 Fetch

36

Solutions 37–38

37

Across:
1 *Play*
3 *Toffs*
7 *Hoop* (Plate of soup)
8 Stereotype
9 Aura
12 Interlopers
13 Erase
15 Hedge
19 Agriculture
21 Euro
23 Initiative
24 Plan
25 Guile
26 Silt

Down:
1 Pestilence
2 Yorkers
3 Trolls
4 Fry-ups
5 Shear
6 Sour
10 Used
11 Antecedent
14 Afar
16 Estates
17 Bikini
18 Futile
20 Going
22 Ugly

38

Across:
1 Bangle
4 Lower (Bangalore)
8 Pepys
9 Impasse
10 Squeeze
11 Menu
12 Nod
14 Feta
15 Even
18 Sky
21 Oboe
23 Onerous
25 Brioche
26 Tripe
27 Terse
28 Adonis

Down:
1 Bypass
2 Neptune
3 Las Vegas
4 Lope
5 Waste
6 Rhesus
7 Vixen
13 Dejected
16 Erosion
17 Sorbet
19 Yokel
20 Assess
22 Osier
24 Acme

Solutions 39–40

39

Across:
1 *Done*
4 *Firm*
8 *Lynn* (Dunfermline)
9 Injurious
11 Senora
13 Uttered
15 Veneer
16 Dashed
18 Strafe
20 Pennon
22 Overdue
23 Fiddle
25 Dreamboat
26 Flew
27 Gosh
28 Razz

Down:
2 Oink
3 Equate
4 Fairer
5 Roused
6 Xylophone
7 Anna
10 Sedated
12 Avis
13 Unbridled
14 Tenfold
17 Dunk
19 Ever so
20 Preach
21 Number
23 Fife
24 Baez

40

Across:
1 Alter
4 Peace (Altarpiece)
10 Orvieto
11 Hyper
12 Radii
13 Berlioz
15 Styx
17 Caber
19 Inset
22 Up to
25 Twitter
27 Impel
29 Fit in
30 Evoking
31 Heart
32 Cease

Down:
2 Livid
3 Elegise
5 Ether
6 Capsize
7 Board
8 Booby
9 Graze
14 Exit
16 True
18 A little
20 Noisome
21 Stiff
23 Pries
24 Elegy
26 Tuner
28 Pains

Solutions 41-42

41

Across:
1 *Agree*
4 *Shun*
7 *Earn* (A Grecian urn)
8 Impolite
9 Snowstorm
10 Bet
12 Attest
14 Lavish
16 Old
18 Barbarian
21 Annoying
22 Oath
23 Beam
24 Naked

Down:
1 Against
2 Renowned
3 Exist
4 Sulk
5 Untie
6 Spiral
11 Overlook
13 Tragic
15 Smarted
17 Lunge
19 Begin
20 Foam

42

Across:
1 Fissure
5 Foul (Fish or fowl)
7 Ounce
8 Permit
10 Play
11 Drawings
13 Issued
14 Potato
17 Together
19 Taxi
21 Curves
22 Theft
23 Heal
24 Lowered

Down:
1 Footprints
2 Sandals
3 Used
4 Expert
5 Firewood
6 Union
9 Associated
12 Festival
15 Amateur
16 Vessel
18 Gauze
20 Stew

Solutions 43-44

43

Across:
1 Pseudo
4 Coup (Sudoku)
8 Absent
9 Yeoman
10 Words
11 Trooper
13 Thou
15 Six
16 Sand
18 Cryptic
20 Cross
23 Come to
24 Ravage
25 Tend
26 Twenty

Down:
1 Pibroch
2 Emend
3 Date
5 Odorous
6 Plane
7 By proxy
12 Ustinov
14 Umpteen
17 Nosegay
19 Roost
21 Raven
22 Brew

44

Across:
7 Struck
8 Chewer (Structure)
9 Golden jubilee
10 Flouting
12 Days
13 Spiv
15 Dustcart
17 Detrimentally
19 Sexton
20 Balzac

Down:
1 Stroll
2 Quadrumvirate
3 Skin
4 Scourges
5 Periodic table
6 Heresy
11 In demand
14 Prefer
16 Reload
18 Nobs

The Telegraph

Solutions 45-46

45

Across:
1 *Holly*
4 *Head*
7 *Isla*
8 *Anglesey* (Holyhead, Isle of Anglesey)
9 Confining
10 Sty
12 Byroad
14 Avenge
16 Ark
18 Masticate
21 Dulcimer
22 Feel
23 West
24 Wales

Down:
1 History
2 Leapfrog
3 Yearn
4 Heed
5 Adept
6 Agenda
11 Merciful
13 Dear me
15 Gutless
17 Rouse
19 Throw
20 Scot

46

Across:
1 *Chicken*
8 *Ticker*
9 *Marsala* (Chicken tikka masala)
11 Abeyance
12 Rebel
14 Enow
15 Poultice
17 Ribaldry
18 Thor
20 Jetty
21 Ditching
23 Tuition
24 Clammy
25 Quarter

Down:
2 Heaven
3 Cashew
4 Ella
5 Bicycle
6 Skintight
7 Freeze-dry
10 Abhorrent
12 Reproduce
13 Booby trap
16 Alchemy
18 Tester
19 Otiose
22 Guru

Solutions 47–48

47

Across:
1 Greece
4 Banned (Greaseband)
7 Outright
9 Atheist
12 Crumb
13 Awful
15 Swing
16 Apart
17 Essay
18 Acute
19 Retrace
23 Advocate
24 Attend
25 Streak

Down:
1 Gloucester
2 Enthusiast
3 Cribbage
4 Butt
5 Nose
6 Eros
8 Ham-fisted
10 Immaculate
11 Turtleneck
14 Layabout
20 Exit
21 Ruse
22 Card

48

Across:
1 Fern
3 Nature (Furniture)
8 Amazing
9 Tease
10 Human
11 Trident
12 Redeem
14 Letter
18 Siamese
20 Trout
22 Utter
23 Ascribe
24 Scored
25 Knit

Down:
1 Feather
2 Realm
3 Negate
4 Tutti
5 Reagent
6 Fiance
7 Vent
13 Drastic
15 Entice
16 Retreat
17 Demand
18 Soup
19 Error
21 Onion

Solutions 49–50

49

Across:
1 Pose
4 Toffees (Post office)
8 Vertical
9 Air
11 Dining
13 Design
14 Third
15 Ends
17 Kept
18 Using
20 Talent
21 Kettle
24 Rig
25 Irritate
26 Satisfy
27 Eyed

Down:
2 Ocean
3 Extent
4 Tick
5 Folded
6 Examine
7 Strengthen
10 Adventures
12 Ghost
13 Drunk
16 Delight
18 Unties
19 Gentle
22 Title
23 Prey

50

Across:
1 Polly
4 Anthers (Polyanthus)
8 Quicker
9 Prize
10 Aggro
11 Asphalt
13 Nosh
15 Torpor
17 Eschew
20 Lump
22 Jostles
24 Raven
26 Datum
27 Fatigue
28 Axolotl
29 Steps

Down:
1 Piquant
2 Lying
3 Yoko Ono
4 Aortas
5 Top up
6 Epitaph
7 Sweat
12 Shem
14 Orle
16 Risotto
18 Sprites
19 Wonders
21 Useful
22 Judea
23 Limbo
25 Vague

Solutions 51–52

51

Across:
1 *Ass*
3 *Wan*
5 *Damn* (Aswan Dam)
7 Ready
8 Savant
10 Aria
11 Maharaja
13 Seaman
14 Nevada
17 Agar-agar
19 Data
21 Alpaca
22 Bar-b-q
23 Papa
24 Aka
25 Mae

Down:
1 Air-marshal
2 Stamina
3 Ways
4 Nassau
5 Deviated
6 Manna
9 Catafalque
12 Lava-lava
15 Anagram
16 Sahara
18 Alloa
20 Abba

52

Across:
1 *Rhea*
4 *List*
8 *Tick* (Realistic)
9 Quickstep
11 Nebula
13 Borodin
15 Florin
16 Caxton
18 Russia
20 Across
22 Drive-in
23 Jingle
25 Youngster
26 Pest
27 Maze
28 Wood

Down:
2 Haul
3 Anchor
4 Lesson
5 Scenic
6 Situation
7 Okra
10 Penance
12 Afar
13 Bossiness
14 Rigidly
17 Nosy
19 Areola
20 Avenge
21 Ripsaw
23 Jape
24 Veto

The Telegraph

Solutions 53-54

53

Across:
1 Plea
3 Scar (Police car)
9 Exude
10 Breakfast
11 Royal
12 Incidence
15 Assume
17 Stench
19 Whirlwind
21 Drank
23 Imitation
24 Bliss
25 Heed
26 Kept

Down:
1 Publican
2 Exercise
4 Chains
5 Retreat
6 Fury
7 Tell
8 Skid
13 Infinite
14 Whodunit
16 Mawkish
18 Virile
20 Loan
21 Debt
22 Arid

54

Across:
1 Waist
4 Thyme (Waste time)
10 Teacher
11 Range
12 Easel
13 Evening
15 Also
17 Opera
19 Twigs
22 Idea
25 Dioxide
27 Ranch
29 Lodge
30 Treated
31 Cycle
32 Study

Down:
2 Arabs
3 Scholar
5 Horse
6 Mending
7 Utter
8 Tries
9 Ledge
14 Vote
16 Laid
18 Proudly
20 Warmest
21 Oddly
23 Death
24 Shade
26 Ideal
28 Noted

Solutions 55-56

55

Across:
1 Inert
4 Rice (In a trice)
8 Dip
9 Privateer
10 Ogre
11 Restless
12 Gas
13 Simply
14 Writes
16 Has
17 Generous
18 Cede
20 Elaborate
21 End
22 Isle
23 Loser

Down:
1 Indoors
2 Experimental
3 Tops
4 Raises
5 Chapters
6 Nevertheless
7 Arms
11 Ray
12 Glorious
14 Was
15 Slender
16 Humane
17 Glen
19 Yell

56

Across:
1 Boss
4 Hanover (Bossa nova)
8 Mixed bag
9 Nap
11 Quarts
13 Altair
14 Elope
15 Arch
17 Zeno
18 Smock
20 Defray
21 Earner
24 Roe
25 Practice
26 Deserve
27 Need

Down:
2 Ouija
3 Svelte
4 Hobo
5 Niggle
6 Vintage
7 Repertoire
10 Squandered
12 Slimy
13 Apace
16 Coffers
18 Sapper
19 Kaftan
22 Niche
23 Wake

Solutions 57–58

57

Across:
1 *Piece*
5 *Agree*
8 *Meant* (Peace agreement)
9 Equip
10 Halfpenny
11 Sue
12 Deteriorate
15 West Country
19 Our
20 Jazziness
22 Eland
23 Ousel
24 Kneel
25 Yolky

Down:
1 Peepshow
2 Exuded
3 Emphatic
4 Sailor
5 Atop
6 Rwanda
7 Edgy
13 Obtusely
14 Everyday
16 Sizzle
17 Unease
18 You-all
20 Jack
21 Idol

58

Across:
1 *Mabel*
4 *Thorpe*
9 *Lincoln*
10 *Sheer* (Mablethorpe Lincolnshire)
11 Calm
12 Raiding
13 Sea
14 Side
16 Gaga
18 Bus
20 Extreme
21 Ammo
24 Comet
25 Crystal
26 Resort
27 Haste

Down:
1 Malice
2 Banal
3 Look
5 Hustings
6 Reeling
7 Enrage
8 Infra
13 Selector
15 Isthmus
17 Fencer
18 Beach
19 Coolie
22 Maths
23 Myth

Solutions 59–60

59

Across:
1 Gray
3 Tape (Great ape)
9 Nacre
10 Roquefort
11 Remit
12 Originate
15 Leeway
17 Stooge
19 Reluctant
21 Mambo
23 Bagatelle
24 Vista
25 Tank
26 Edgy

Down:
1 Gargoyle
2 Acquired
4 Anorak
5 Entreat
6 Scam
7 West
8 Yeti
13 So-called
14 Leathery
16 Acrobat
18 Flagon
20 Cite
21 Move
22 Mist

60

Across:
1 Purr
4 Chess (Purchase)
8 Belittle
9 Iffy
10 Stay
11 Notional
12 Trance
14 Wrench
16 Burglary
19 Cape
20 Fair
21 Bracelet
22 Evade
23 Dupe

Down:
2 Unity
3 Retinue
4 Crest
5 Episode
6 Sofia
7 Hector
13 Nigeria
14 Wayward
15 Cipher
17 Usage
18 Amble
19 Cheap

Solutions 61–62

61

Across:
1 Chuckle
5 Hates (Chocolates)
8 Event
9 Operate
10 Mysteries
12 Ill
13 Resist
14 Period
17 Bee
18 Accidents
20 Integer
21 Enemy
23 Hides
24 Disease

Down:
1 Cream
2 Use
3 Kittens
4 Exotic
5 Heeds
6 Tradition
7 Swelled
11 Suspected
13 Rubbish
15 Endless
16 Scared
18 Aegis
19 Style
22 Era

62

Across:
1 Cheque
4 Points (Checkpoints)
7 A la carte
9 Updated
12 Sepia
13 Rioja
15 Furze
16 Rural
17 Sprig
18 Unarm
19 Deejays
23 Vehement
24 Welles
25 Static

Down:
1 Classified
2 Exasperate
3 Unawares
4 Peep
5 Iowa
6 Take
8 Tudor rose
10 Tournament
11 Diplomatic
14 Argument
20 Elbe
21 Jail
22 Yves

Solutions 63-64

63

Across:
1 *New*
3 *Dis*
5 *Beech* (Nudist beach)
8 Molar
9 Unusual
10 Daze
11 Fragment
13 Jerkin
14 Voyeur
17 Per annum
19 Flap
22 Tramcar
23 Level
24 Rhyme
25 Wax
26 Nay

Down:
1 Nomad
2 Waltzer
3 Dark
4 Squirm
5 Bludgeon
6 Exude
7 Holster
12 Pinnacle
13 Jupiter
15 Enliven
16 Burrow
18 Ready
20 Pally
21 Flux

64

Across:
4 Baring
7 Straight (Bering Strait)
8 Utopia
10 Require
11 Seal
13 Festival
14 Weld
16 Alto
18 Transact
19 Once
21 Gearbox
22 Uproot
24 Headcase
25 Tiddly

Down:
1 Ethereal
2 Valuation
3 Aggravate
4 B T U
5 Impale
6 Glazed
9 Tie
11 Sleazebag
12 Awestruck
15 Lacrosse
16 Adjust
17 Torrid
20 Coo
23 Thy

The Telegraph

Solutions 65–66

65

Across:
1 *Auk*
3 *Sure*
5 *Near* (Auctioneer)
8 Menacing
10 Acts
11 Sad
13 Ripen
14 Semblance
16 Pry
17 Din
19 Negligent
21 Attic
22 And
24 Nick
25 Malinger
26 Dolt
27 Mean
28 Dim

Down:
1 Arms
2 Kind
3 Succulence
4 Renown
6 Escapade
7 Resonant
9 Eager
12 Prediction
14 Sprained
15 Mystical
18 Inane
20 Gyrate
22 Aged
23 Dram

66

Across:
1 *Loo*
3 *Seal*
5 *Bawl* (Lucille Ball)
8 Scabbard
10 Shun
11 All
13 Chess
14 Antarctic
16 Tea
17 Elm
19 Brasserie
21 Lodge
22 Era
24 Troy
25 Cadillac
26 Crib
27 Barn
28 Axe

Down:
1 Lisa
2 Oral
3 Subscribed
4 Arrest
6 Achiever
7 Lonesome
9 Clone
12 Accusation
14 Athletic
15 Tandoori
18 Libra
20 Armada
22 Elba
23 Ache

Solutions 67-68

67

Across:
1 Pollen
4 Easier (Polynesia)
7 Increase
9 Cradles
12 Comic
13 Ideas
15 Paths
16 Event
17 Eaten
18 Tease
19 Species
23 Attitude
24 Recess
25 Assent

Down:
1 Principles
2 Locomotive
3 Exercise
4 Ever
5 Sand
6 Edge
8 Scientist
10 Literature
11 Settlement
14 Sentries
20 Pine
21 Care
22 Ears

68

Across:
7 Moaner
8 Leaser (Mona Lisa)
10 Rake-off
11 Trent
12 Scab
13 Heavy
17 Derby
18 Heel
22 Apart
23 Croquet
24 Poodle
25 Decade

Down:
1 Ambrose
2 Jackdaw
3 Devon
4 Festive
5 Usher
6 Crete
9 Offenbach
14 Textile
15 Regular
16 Blitzed
19 Happy
20 Aaron
21 Moses

Solutions 69–70

69

Across:
1 *Terry*
4 *Tory*
7 *Real*
8 *Disputes* (Territorial disputes)
9 Smuggling
10 Gym
12 Blotch
14 Tea bag
16 Aft
18 Scapa Flow
21 Quotient
22 Oryx
23 Jazz
24 Piece

Down:
1 Thermal
2 Relegate
3 Yodel
4 Trug
5 Reedy
6 Usenet
11 Calf-love
13 Hockey
15 Acolyte
17 Fauna
19 Put up
20 A to Z

70

Across:
1 *Czech*
4 *Point*
10 *Charlie* (Checkpoint Charlie)
11 Cutie
12 Besom
13 Asexual
15 Nest
17 Lloyd
19 Oomph
22 Gown
25 Marilyn
27 Equip
29 Sleet
30 Emerald
31 Sylph
32 After

Down:
2 Z Cars
3 Calumny
5 On cue
6 No-trump
7 Scuba
8 Vegas
9 Jelly
14 Stow
16 Edgy
18 Larceny
20 Oneself
21 Smash
23 Onset
24 Spade
26 Let up
28 Usage

Solutions 71-72

71

Across:
1 Knight
4 Sites (Night sights)
8 Super
9 Engaged
10 Erosion
11 Free
12 Sea
14 Deal
15 Tyre
18 Eye
21 Unit
23 Allowed
25 Gradual
26 Trial
27 Dread
28 Screws

Down:
1 Kisses
2 Improve
3 Horrible
4 Sigh
5 Tiger
6 Sudden
7 Means
13 Athletic
16 Rewrite
17 Rugged
19 Eagle
20 Adults
22 Image
24 Fund

72

Across:
1 Suite
4 Meet (Sweetmeat)
8 Pot
9 Salamanca
10 Oven
11 Scenario
12 Ape
13 Trauma
14 Sonnet
16 Sun
17 Practice
18 Demo
20 Pachyderm
21 Ebb
22 Stun
23 Metre

Down:
1 Support
2 In the balance
3 Easy
4 Malice
5 Edmonton
6 Infringement
7 Halo
11 Spa
12 Amethyst
14 Sue
15 Trouble
16 Screen
17 Pipe
19 Imam

The Telegraph

Solutions 73–74

73

Across:
1 Simper
4 Thighs (Sympathise)
7 Bitterly
9 Islands
12 Tooth
13 Areas
15 Nylon
16 Exist
17 Trout
18 Theme
19 Suspect
23 Assemble
24 Hoards
25 Upsets

Down:
1 Substances
2 Motionless
3 Elephant
4 Toys
5 Idea
6 Hold
8 Lifeboats
10 Noticeable
11 Subtleness
14 Settle up
20 Undo
21 Poor
22 Caps

74

Across:
1 *Mass*
3 *Turk*
9 *Eight* (Masticate)
10 Eglantine
11 Noyes
12 North Pole
15 Squawk
17 Strobe
19 Beseeched
21 Fakes
23 Interlude
24 Roost
25 Ever
26 Asps

Down:
1 Meekness
2 Solarium
4 Unison
5 Keenest
6 Ugly
7 Otis
8 Inch
13 Jodhpurs
14 Deadness
16 Website
18 Tsetse
20 Ezra
21 Fort
22 Knox

Solutions 75-76

75

Across:
1 *Gas*
3 *Trick*
6 *Flu* (Gastric flu)
8 Virgo
9 Jonquil
10 Ramshackle
12 Yaw
15 Only
17 Rave
18 Eat
22 Magnum opus
25 Oatmeal
26 Usage
27 Zip
28 Texan
29 End

Down:
1 Governor
2 Scramble
3 Trophy
4 Inject
5 Kindly
6 Foul
7 Ugly
11 Ear
13 Warplane
14 Bedstead
16 Yam
19 Talent
20 Influx
21 Impugn
23 Boaz
24 Stop

76

Across:
1 Nether
4 Landau (Netherlander)
7 Antennae
9 Fretsaw
12 Overt
13 Emeer
15 Iraqi
16 End-on
17 Nudes
18 Euros
19 Nostrum
23 Spare rib
24 Danger
25 The Box

Down:
1 Neapolitan
2 Title pages
3 Einstein
4 Leer
5 Next
6 Alga
8 After-damp
10 Spider crab
11 Witness box
14 Research
20 Okra
21 Twig
22 User

Solutions 77–78

77

Across:
1 *Sly*
3 *Tough*
6 *And* (Sleight of hand)
8 Meant
9 Avarice
10 Annihilate
12 Has
15 Hunt
17 Thin
18 Got
22 Punishment
25 Extinct
26 Alien
27 Yob
28 Lurch
29 Hue

Down:
1 Sympathy
2 Yearning
3 Tetchy
4 Unable
5 Health
6 Arid
7 Died
11 Eat
13 Sheepish
14 Instance
16 Top
19 Tunnel
20 Bitter
21 Thrash
23 Deny
24 Stab

78

Across:
1 Marshal
5 Lore (Martial law)
7 Later
8 Strive
10 Free
11 Personal
13 Catchy
14 Euston
17 Occasion
19 Firm
21 Plaice
22 Green
23 Joke
24 Theatre

Down:
1 Malefactor
2 Retreat
3 Hurl
4 Listen
5 Larkspur
6 Raven
9 Blancmange
12 Cheshire
15 Trident
16 Covert
18 Cello
20 Ogre

Solutions 79-80

79

Across:
4 Revert
5 Hems (River Thames)
7 Grandma
10 Gifts
11 Teacher
12 Newer
14 Figures
15 Valid
16 Several
20 Paths
21 Delight
22 Yank
23 Retire

Down:
1 Event
2 Aroma
3 Desires
4 Rare
6 Settee
8 Derides
9 Accused
10 General
13 Malady
14 Fishing
17 Refer
18 Licit
19 Shoe

80

Across:
1 Fault
5 Heard (Faltered)
8 Imago
9 Assam
10 Obnoxious
11 Oaf
12 Ecofriendly
15 Showstopper
19 Aim
20 John Keats
22 Union
23 Truer
24 Zadie
25 Enemy

Down:
1 Flavours
2 Unsafe
3 Timorous
4 Wagner
5 Hoax
6 Abroad
7 Doss
13 Exposure
14 Yeomanry
16 On hold
17 Opaque
18 Racine
20 Jazz
21 Kite

Solutions 81–82

81

Across:
1 *Inn*
3 *Fury*
5 *Hate* (Infuriate)
8 Eighteen
10 Hype
11 Ago
13 Ouija
14 Soul music
16 Cox
17 Aid
19 Beer belly
21 Moral
22 Eel
24 Took
25 Wizardry
26 Rasp
27 Bevy
28 Toe

Down:
1 Idea
2 No-go
3 Fathomable
4 Rhesus
6 Atypical
7 Eye candy
9 Igloo
12 Vocabulary
14 Scimitar
15 Uxorious
18 Iller
20 Equine
22 Edit
23 Lyre

82

Across:
1 *Quay*
5 *Hole*
7 *Surgery* (Keyhole surgery)
8 Porridge
10 Rich
12 Eggy
14 Overgrow
16 Unlawful
17 Nail
18 Jamb
19 Asbestos
22 Old Nick
23 Teak
24 East

Down:
1 Quip
2 Yser
3 Trade-off
4 Mere
5 Hydrogen
6 Each
9 Organza
11 Chorizo
13 Yearbook
15 Ex libris
18 Jilt
19 Aida
20 Sake
21 Soot

Solutions 83-84

83

Across:
1 Korea
4 Wrist (Careerist)
10 Traipse
11 Curry
12 Friar
13 Soprano
15 Open
17 Chore
19 Usher
22 Rest
25 Oatcake
27 Angel
29 Capri
30 Idiotic
31 Steep
32 Happy

Down:
2 Okapi
3 Emperor
5 Recap
6 Surface
7 Staff
8 Cease
9 Pylon
14 Onus
16 Perk
18 Hot spot
20 Stamina
21 Pouch
23 Eerie
24 Pluck
26 Agile
28 Get-up

84

Across:
1 Writes
4 Ought (Right sort)
8 Disco
9 Actions
10 Sharing
11 Mere
12 Eat
14 Stun
15 Huts
18 Sea
21 Owls
23 Control
25 Reserve
26 Irate
27 Shown
28 Ignore

Down:
1 Widest
2 Instant
3 Emotions
4 Oats
5 Globe
6 Tastes
7 Gauge
13 Thinking
16 Tornado
17 Courts
19 Acres
20 Sleeve
22 Lasso
24 Gran

Solutions 85-86

85

Across:
1 Accede
5 Hence (Accidents)
9 Broadcast
10 Tip
11 Run
12 Neighbour
14 Van
16 Stage
18 Sum
19 Apartment
21 Man
22 Ice
23 Orchestra
25 Notes
26 Theory

Down:
2 Crown
3 Endings
4 Era
5 Hatch
6 Nations
7 Experimental
8 Abbreviation
13 Image
15 Nearest
17 Extreme
20 Tools
21 Motor
24 Cot

86

Across:
1 Barque
4 Hoad (Barcode)
9 Paved
10 Ju-jitsu
11 Danseur
12 Choir
13 Whence
15 Ossify
18 Craze
20 Gabriel
23 Emotion
24 Grasp
25 Lute
26 Fleece

Down:
1 Biped
2 Revenue
3 Undue
5 Objects
6 Ditto
7 Fjord
8 Quarry
13 Wicked
14 Coexist
16 Imitate
17 Agony
19 Atoll
21 Bagel
22 Lapse

Solutions 87–88

87

Across:
1 *Cam*
3 *Eau*
5 *Mile*
7 *Tease* (Camomile teas)
8 Cassis
10 Omit
11 Microdot
13 Eggnog
14 Coffee
17 Limekiln
19 Snug
21 Eclair
22 Punch
23 Pail
24 Tot
25 Eon

Down:
1 Citronella
2 Moaning
3 Ever
4 Urchin
5 Mushroom
6 Laird
9 Strengthen
12 Cocktail
15 Finance
16 Claret
18 Mocha
20 Spat

88

Across:
1 Often
4 Bark (Offenbach)
8 Unbowed
9 Hyper
10 Ensue
11 Tobacco
13 Shovel
15 Facade
17 Tramcar
20 Undid
22 Rocky
23 Scupper
24 Juan
25 Liner

Down:
1 Of use
2 Tabasco sauce
3 Nowhere
4 Bidet
5 Rehab
6 Spick and span
7 Brooke
12 Off
13 Saturn
14 Lea
16 As usual
18 Coypu
19 Risen
21 Durer

Solutions 89–90

Across:
1 Singer
4 Pour (Singapore)
9 Admit
10 Fatigue
11 Mistake
12 Inert
13 Costly
15 Leader
18 Socks
20 Goggles
23 Oration
24 Argue
25 Huge
26 Rental

Down:
1 Swarm
2 Nemesis
3 Extra
5 Outside
6 Rogue
7 After
8 Better
13 Cosmos
14 Lasting
16 Delight
17 Agony
19 Coach
21 Glaze
22 Steal

89

Across:
1 Myrrh
4 Curie (Mercury)
8 Nap
9 Greasepaint
10 Termite
12 Equal
13 Simper
14 Impala
17 Swift
19 Lenient
21 Deerstalker
23 Ire
24 Rummy
25 Angle

Down:
1 Might
2 Rye
3 Hostile
4 Copper
5 Raise
6 Entourage
7 Ophelia
11 Remainder
13 Sustain
15 Montana
16 Classy
18 Therm
20 Terse
22 Keg

90

Solutions 91–92

91

Across:
1 Blown
4 Effuse (Blown a fuse)
7 Outward
8 Ruin
10 Moose
11 Royalty
14 Stew
16 Twenty
18 Latest
21 Pass
23 Chapter
26 Spear
27 Hone
28 Tornado
29 Static
30 Dates

Down:
1 Broomstick
2 Outcome
3 Nearest
4 Endure
5 Ferry
6 Skill
9 Mysterious
12 Owls
13 Ant
15 Type
17 Nap
19 Assured
20 Elegant
22 Arctic
24 Adopt
25 Treat

92

Across:
1 Tester
4 Monies (Testimonies)
7 Conjured
9 Nemesis
12 Email
13 Ivied
15 Talks
16 Error
17 Excel
18 Awful
19 Essence
23 Advances
24 Breath
25 Geyser

Down:
1 Ticker tape
2 Santa Claus
3 Equalise
4 Mode
5 Nape
6 Etui
8 Encircled
10 Sacrifices
11 Steriliser
14 Delaware
20 Sour
21 Ezra
22 Cash

The Telegraph

Solutions 93–94

93

Across:
1 *Here*
5 *Rose*
7 *Welcome* (Hero's welcome)
8 Arbroath
10 Wave
12 Ecru
14 Sticking
16 Pizzeria
17 Nosh
18 Keep
19 Greeting
22 Embrace
23 Shod
24 Mash

Down:
1 Hiya
2 Ewer
3 Cleanser
4 Loch
5 Reawaken
6 Edge
9 Receive
11 Venison
13 Unzipped
15 I dare say
18 Kiss
19 Go by
20 Teem
21 Gush

94

Across:
1 Furze
4 Trait (First rate)
8 Sad
9 Mobile phone
10 Relapse
12 Riser
13 Sextet
14 Waffle
17 Narco
19 Enjoyed
21 Overindulge
23 You
24 Swank
25 Email

Down:
1 Femur
2 Rub
3 Eclipse
4 Topper
5 Amour
6 Tsetse fly
7 Adverse
11 Luxurious
13 Synonym
15 Adjudge
16 Bewick
18 Omega
20 Dwell
22 Lea

Solutions 95–96

95

Across:
1 Speck
4 Tater (Spectator)
8 Emu
9 Good-looking
10 Toby jug
12 Geese
13 Embryo
14 Baffle
17 Solid
19 Trifler
21 Information
23 Rag
24 Hedge
25 Empty

Down:
1 Sight
2 Ego
3 Killjoy
4 Trough
5 Tying
6 Regretful
7 Austere
11 Bobsleigh
13 Ensnare
15 Agitate
16 Sterne
18 Dyfed
20 Runny
22 Imp

96

Across:
1 Marten
4 of fire (Martin Offiah)
7 Laywoman
9 Skipper
12 Islam
13 Idaho
15 Great
16 balls
17 Yours
19 Tenon
20 Try it on
24 Baguette
25 In love
26 At odds

Down:
1 Melting pot
2 Royal jelly
3 Enormity
4 Oink
5 Flip
6 Race
8 Asia
10 Pollinated
11 Reasonless
14 Obstruct
18 Ulna
21 Rain
22 Into
23 Oboe

The Telegraph

Solutions 97–98

97

Across:
1 *Court*
4 *Inert*
8 *Rap* (Caught in a trap)
9 Vinaigrette
10 License
12 Rates
13 Errors
14 Intend
17 Roots
19 Equator
21 Illustrated
23 Sat
24 Yarns
25 Layer

Down:
1 Civil
2 Urn
3 Thinner
4 Israel
5 Enter
6 Treatment
7 Opposed
11 Curiosity
13 Earnest
15 Neutral
16 Beasts
18 Solar
20 Rider
22 Try

98

Across:
1 Concert
5 Inner (Concertina)
8 Serif
9 Emigrés
10 Enhance
11 Iraqi
12 Juliet
14 Employ
17 Cobra
19 Assizes
22 Drastic
23 Purse
24 Wield
25 Liaison

Down:
1 Caste
2 Narwhal
3 Elfin
4 Tiered
5 Iridium
6 Norma
7 Riskily
12 Jackdaw
13 Exalted
15 Lazarus
16 Rascal
18 Brave
20 Sepia
21 Sheen

Solutions 99–100

Solutions 101–102

101

Across:
1 Fort
3 Hops (Four Tops)
9 Idiot
10 Revulsion
11 Creep
12 Clearance
15 Speech
17 Demean
19 Opportune
21 Tacit
23 Hurricane
24 Chase
25 Seem
26 Meet

Down:
1 Forecast
2 Reviewed
4 Orient
5 Sincere
6 Fine
7 Stop
8 Blur
13 Regulate
14 Interest
16 Clothes
18 Sparse
20 Ruin
21 Tact
22 Chat

102

Across:
1 *Shoe*
4 *Pace*
8 *Tree* (Choux pastry)
9 Battalion
11 Saloon
13 Cricket
15 Jeremy
16 Duress
18 Rather
20 Salute
22 Nonplus
23 Accost
25 Ethelbert
26 Ruse
27 Once
28 Rhea

Down:
2 Hear
3 Entire
4 Policy
5 Closed
6 Erroneous
7 Mean
10 Natural
12 Ajar
13 Criticism
14 Immense
17 Stew
19 Rotten
20 Sphere
21 Lumber
23 Agra
24 Brie

Solutions 103–104

103

Across:
1 Goes
4 Tories (Ghost stories)
7 Era
9 Scar
10 Stinging
11 Vet
12 Asia
13 Election
16 Contributions
19 Farewell
23 Seer
24 Axe
25 Classics
26 Chef
27 Eft
28 Closer
29 Sett

Down:
2 Occasionally
3 Servant
4 Taste
5 Raise
6 Eight
8 Announcement
14 Label
15 Cot
17 Row
18 Insects
20 Easel
21 Exits
22 Laser

104

Across:
1 Rice
5 Mile (Wry smile)
7 Palermo
8 Moccasin
10 Quay
12 Zulu
14 Fieriest
16 de Gaulle
17 Oink
18 Stoa
19 John Bull
22 Expanse
23 Moss
24 Weed

Down:
1 Roam
2 Epic
3 Blissful
4 Wren
5 Mosquito
6 Envy
9 Opulent
11 Arsenal
13 Unawares
15 Elephant
18 Scum
19 Jape
20 Brew
21 Loud

Solutions 105–106

105

Across:
1 *Borne*
5 *Tubby*
8 *Wilde* (Born to be wild)
9 Movie
10 Light meal
11 Ell
12 Tempestuous
15 Palm Springs
19 Ida
20 Jack Sprat
22 Utter
23 Later
24 Zorro
25 End-on

Down:
1 Bumped up
2 Revolt
3 Ewe-lambs
4 Plague
5 Text
6 Bolero
7 Yawl
13 Tincture
14 Squadron
16 Locker
17 Rarity
18 Sifted
20 Jazz
21 Silo

106

Across:
1 *Reek*
3 *Clue*
9 *Sieve* (Reclusive)
10 Lethargic
11 Handy
12 Xylophone
15 Needle
17 Assize
19 Queue-jump
21 Adieu
23 Endurance
24 Aloof
25 Yolk
26 Omit

Down:
1 Relaxing
2 Extolled
4 Legion
5 Eschews
6 Tern
7 Deny
8 Ramp
13 Viburnum
14 Helpmeet
16 Liquefy
18 Feudal
20 Earl
21 Ajar
22 Iron

Solutions 107–108

107

108

Solutions 109–110

109

Across:
1 Ghost
4 Rate (Go straight)
8 Bid
9 Receiving
10 Elan
11 Openings
12 Die
13 School
14 Cliffs
16 Foe
17 Promptly
18 Scar
20 Obedience
21 Nap
22 Uses
23 Dress

Down:
1 Goblets
2 Old-fashioned
3 Tart
4 Recipe
5 Triangle
6 Significance
7 Ages
11 Oil
12 Dolphins
14 Coy
15 Stripes
16 Flings
17 Prod
19 Feud

110

Across:
1 Miss
3 Terriers (Mysterious)
9 Jonah
10 Umbrage
11 Raw
13 Satellite
14 Potash
16 Caress
18 Arriviste
20 Sad
22 Charlie
23 Ritzy
25 Rallying
26 Open

Down:
1 Major
2 Son
4 Equity
5 Rubella
6 Examiners
7 Shekels
8 Thus
12 Waterfall
14 Prancer
15 Saveloy
17 Astern
19 Eire
21 Doyen
24 Tip

Solutions 111–112

111

Across:
1 *Ree*
3 *Per*
5 *Cuss*
7 *Shuns* (Repercussions)
8 Jalopy
10 Bony
11 Schmaltz
13 Luxury
14 Stamen
17 Tumbling
19 Anil
21 Cudgel
22 Heavy
23 Knee
24 Wad
25 Air

Down:
1 Risibility
2 Equinox
3 Push
4 Reject
5 Calamity
6 Sepal
9 Ozone layer
12 Prologue
15 Montana
16 Inflow
18 Mourn
20 Shed

112

Across:
1 Barbie
4 Queued (Barbecued)
7 Macaroni
9 Azimuth
12 Axing
13 Aglow
15 Draft
16 Recto
17 Exile
18 Crude
19 Khedive
23 Escapism
24 Jet set
25 Geodic

Down:
1 Bombay duck
2 Receivable
3 Irrigate
4 Quiz
5 Edam
6 Emit
8 Nail files
10 Unoccupied
11 Hypodermic
14 Wreckage
20 Hide
21 Dais
22 Vent

Solutions 113–114

113

Across:
1 Bare
3 Route (Beirut)
7 Load
8 Disposable
9 Chew
12 Assassinate
13 Grant
15 Chore
19 Illusionist
21 Dose
23 Astounding
24 Less
25 Terse
26 Glut

Down:
1 Bedraggled
2 Explain
3 Resist
4 Urbane
5 Elect
6 Cage
10 Hero
11 Watertight
14 Axis
16 Hangdog
17 Punter
18 Minute
20 Least
22 Omen

114

Across:
1 Flee
3 Choler (Flea collar)
9 Isthmus
10 Apart
11 Gun
12 Existence
13 Astute
14 Target
16 Conundrum
19 Rut
21 Apron
22 Funfair
23 Claret
24 Zero

Down:
1 Fling
2 Extinct
4 Heart-warming
5 Learn
6 Retreat
7 Impertinence
8 Asti
13 Archaic
15 Garbage
17 Norma
18 Rift
20 Torso

Solutions 115–116

115

Across:
1 Ghetto
4 Ferret (Get over it)
7 Alphabet
9 Selfish
12 Seals
13 Fears
15 Abide
16 Clump
17 Ruler
18 Eaten
19 Saddles
23 Champion
24 Bamboo
25 Adults

Down:
1 Grasslands
2 Emphasised
3 Transfer
4 Fate
5 Reef
6 Ends
8 Establish
10 Industrial
11 Happenings
14 Screamed
20 Aura
21 Dumb
22 Echo

116

Across:
1 Lined
4 Answer (Line dancer)
9 Lexicon
10 Jaffa
11 Tint
12 Singlet
13 Vat
14 Feta
16 Kiss
18 Sly
20 Oblique
21 Ecru
24 Capri
25 Zombies
26 Seethe
27 Spoor

Down:
1 Lolita
2 Nixon
3 Duck
5 Nijinsky
6 Waffles
7 Rialto
8 Angst
13 Vanquish
15 Eclipse
17 Coccus
18 Seize
19 Hussar
22 Cairo
23 Imps

The Telegraph

Solutions 117–118

117

Across:
1 *Hike*
4 *Owe*
6 *Miss*
8 *Sooner* (High Commissioner)
9 Maxima
10 Barbados
11 Pelt
12 Made to measure
17 Bust
19 Graduate
22 Pigpen
23 Lulled
24 Jazz
25 Coy
26 Rote

Down:
2 Imola
3 Ennoble
4 Oared
5 En masse
6 Mix-up
7 Simpler
10 Bum
13 Alumina
14 Organic
15 Squalor
16 Eve
18 Topaz
20 Allay
21 Theft

118

Across:
1 Coining
8 Affrays (Coining a phrase)
9 Jabot
10 High altar
11 Lab
12 Exact
13 Sulky
14 Waver
16 Azure
19 Tab
20 Flashbulb
22 Brava
23 Earache
24 Thereby

Down:
1 Cajole
2 Imbibe
3 In the air
4 Gadget
5 Offa
6 Cartel
7 Osprey
13 Squabble
14 Wafted
15 Viagra
16 Amulet
17 Ethane
18 Abbacy
21 Hack

Solutions 119-120

Across:
4 Hoarse
5 Hare (Horsehair)
7 Fiancee
9 Pinch
10 Tan
11 Era
13 Orbit
15 Miracle
16 Rodin
17 New
18 End
21 Treat
22 Digress
23 Weed
24 Deploy

Down:
1 Taint
2 Ashen
3 Caviare
4 Hail
6 Euclid
8 Cabinet
9 Prolong
12 May
14 Sorrow
15 Minaret
18 Eiger
19 Droll
20 Espy

119

Across:
1 Sioux
3 Denise (Sudanese)
7 Nightmare
9 Riot
10 Knee
11 Kneel
13 B-movie
14 Lemon
15 Visor
17 Debris
20 Value
21 Maul
23 Ogle
24 Solitaire
25 Deepen
26 Pygmy

Down:
1 Scarab
2 Unit
3 Damsel
4 Nark
5 Easel
6 Phone
7 Notorious
8 Entourage
11 Kirov
12 Levee
16 Ration
17 Dumas
18 Sherry
19 Amend
22 Loop
23 Orly

120

Solutions 121–122

121

Across:
1 Hearse
5 Preys (Hairsprays)
9 Standards
10 Cap
11 Ore
12 Collector
14 Ire
16 Draft
18 Spa
19 Hesitated
21 Ilk
22 Era
23 Brilliant
25 Tryst
26 Purges

Down:
2 Erase
3 Reduced
4 Ear
5 Paste
6 Excites
7 Supermarkets
8 Astonishment
13 Leapt
15 Ecstasy
17 Tiddler
20 Tibet
21 Image
24 Imp

122

Across:
1 *Sen*
3 *Tin*
5 *Hell* (Sentinel)
7 Ogres
8 Widget
10 Knox
11 Jacobean
13 Ensign
14 Jetsam
17 Euphoric
19 Bull
21 Finish
22 Relay
23 Levy
24 Pig
25 Dud

Down:
1 Shopkeeper
2 Nervous
3 Task
4 Newman
5 Hydrogen
6 Liege
9 Unemployed
12 Ignominy
15 Squalid
16 Bishop
18 Prize
20 Brag

Solutions 123–124

123

Across:
1 *Fun*
3 *Dam*
5 *Meant*
8 *A-list* (Fundamentalist)
9 Succour
10 Knit
11 Julienne
13 Waylay
14 Embryo
17 Dogfight
19 Zeta
22 Wriggle
23 Vouch
24 Rally
25 Yew
26 Kid

Down:
1 Frank
2 Noisily
3 Duty
4 Masque
5 Machismo
6 Acorn
7 Torpedo
12 Taxingly
13 Widower
15 Roebuck
16 Cheeky
18 Grill
20 Aphid
21 Avow

124

Across:
1 Stirling
8 Silver (Sterling silver)
9 Expect
10 Rehearse
11 Sneeze
13 Pressing
17 Bone-idle
20 Carafe
23 Pamphlet
25 Inkpot
26 Cut off
27 Treading

Down:
2 Toxin
3 Reeve
4 Intrepid
5 G S O H
6 Always
7 Lesson
11 Scab
12 Eden
14 Elective
15 Iona
16 Gate
18 Opaque
19 Employ
21 Raked
22 Frown
24 Loft

The Telegraph

Solutions 125–126

125

Across:
1 Errors
4 Myth (Aerosmith)
8 Obtain
9 Classy
10 Brisk
11 Drunken
13 Moor
15 Woe
16 Dirt
18 Company
20 Slope
23 Denial
24 Madden
25 Exam
26 Agrees

Down:
1 Embargo
2 Roams
3 Rant
5 Yearned
6 Haste
7 Scarper
12 Dwindle
14 Replica
17 Repress
19 Obese
21 Ledge
22 Smug

126

Across:
1 Crow
3 Asia (Croatia)
9 Valet
10 Lassitude
11 Reach
12 Melodrama
15 Titian
17 Deluge
19 Repudiate
21 Cobra
23 Heartless
24 Tosca
25 Mend
26 Stud

Down:
1 Calamity
2 Obsolete
4 Squeal
5 Average
6 Ulna
7 Itch
8 Hind
13 Budapest
14 Released
16 Abraham
18 Sprain
20 Date
21 Cats
22 Base

Solutions 127-128

127

128

Solutions 129–130

129

Across:
1 *Purr*
4 *Coll*
8 *Late* (Percolate)
9 Permeated
11 Lurdan
13 Logbook
15 Hoodoo
16 Wetter
18 Filter
20 Coffee
22 Thermit
23 Goalie
25 Asparagus
26 Seep
27 Isle
28 Ooze

Down:
2 Used
3 Ramrod
4 Crambo
5 Lie low
6 Candytuft
7 Fern
10 Dukedom
12 Chef
13 Low-loader
14 Godetia
17 Reed
19 Rhesus
20 Crease
21 Figaro
23 Gosh
24 Buzz

130

Across:
1 Gopher
5 Broke (Go for broke)
9 Innkeeper
10 Axe
11 Dip
12 Tall story
14 Elf
16 Paris
18 Leo
19 Tennessee
21 Off
22 Can
23 Solitaire
25 Steal
26 Worker

Down:
2 Own up
3 Heeltap
4 Rip
5 Burns
6 On a roll
7 Every so often
8 Fiddlesticks
13 Lords
15 Finance
17 Sweater
20 Easel
21 On ice
24 Low

Solutions 131–132

131

Across:
1 Flee
5 Pitt (Flea pit)
7 Traduce
8 Signpost
10 Inch
12 Tiff
14 Enshrine
16 Patience
17 Exit
18 Deep
19 Chickpea
22 Refrain
23 Edgy
24 Tilt

Down:
1 Fuss
2 Eton
3 Napoleon
4 Just
5 Pedigree
6 Tosh
9 Imitate
11 Concise
13 Frippery
15 Sheridan
18 Dive
19 Cafe
20 Kent
21 Aunt

132

Across:
1 Knight
4 Thyme (Nighttime)
8 Stamp
9 Handled
10 Evident
11 Uses
12 Oak
14 Mere
15 Nose
18 Dad
21 Robe
23 Raccoon
25 Gradual
26 Image
27 Needs
28 Agreed

Down:
1 Kisses
2 Imagine
3 Happened
4 Tone
5 Yolks
6 Eldest
7 Photo
13 Knocking
16 Storage
17 Dragon
19 Drill
20 Intend
22 Brave
24 Buds

The Telegraph

Solutions 133–134

133

Across:
1 Peers
4 Tears (Pierced ears)
10 Rattled
11 Glade
12 Drama
13 Enemies
15 Side
17 Linen
19 Angel
22 Tore
25 Envelop
27 Eager
29 Acted
30 Relieve
31 Edged
32 Edits

Down:
2 Extra
3 Release
5 Eagle
6 Realise
7 Crude
8 Added
9 Sense
14 Near
16 Into
18 Invited
20 Needled
21 Relax
23 Opera
24 Armed
26 Lodge
28 Guest

134

Across:
1 Varies
4 Hilly (Very silly)
8 Zebra
9 Octagon
10 Entwine
11 Erse
12 Yap
14 Acne
15 Oath
18 Elf
21 Rich
23 Equable
25 Beijing
26 Arose
27 Sabot
28 Mended

Down:
1 Vizier
2 Robotic
3 Examinee
4 Hate
5 Lager
6 Yankee
7 Money
13 Populace
16 Tabloid
17 Erebus
19 Feign
20 Aeneid
22 Climb
24 Kilt

Solutions 135-136

Solutions 137–138

137

Across:
1 Pay
3 Perch
6 Ace (Paper chase)
8 Allot
9 Married
10 Extinguish
12 Sob
15 Undo
17 Gush
18 Elk
22 Diminutive
25 Maudlin
26 Greet
27 Gut
28 Reply
29 Sun

Down:
1 Peaceful
2 Yuletide
3 Potent
4 Rumour
5 Harass
6 Arid
7 Eddy
11 Hog
13 Business
14 Threaten
16 Old
19 Killer
20 Kidnap
21 Hungry
23 Smug
24 Bust

138

Across:
1 Weld
4 Rest (Well dressed)
8 Stag
9 Hilarious
11 Plucky
13 Coterie
15 Moaned
16 Despot
18 Dieppe
20 Feeler
22 Endorse
23 Robust
25 Trattoria
26 Mars
27 Dear
28 Take

Down:
2 Evil
3 Dragon
4 Raised
5 Stupid
6 Stockpile
7 Ugly
10 Sleeper
12 Amid
13 Camembert
14 Tempest
17 Tory
19 Entree
20 Foster
21 Escort
23 Rome
24 Pick

Solutions 139–140

139

Across:
1 Pause
4 Whole (Poor soul)
10 Purpose
11 Tight
12 Exalt
13 Villain
15 Ever
17 Opera
19 Often
22 Tone
25 Protest
27 Above
29 Oiled
30 Effects
31 Smart
32 Alarm

Down:
2 Aorta
3 Shorter
5 Hotel
6 Luggage
7 Speed
8 Serve
9 Stung
14 Iron
16 Vats
18 Problem
20 Fearful
21 Spoon
23 Other
24 Least
26 Elder
28 Occur

140

Across:
1 Kitsch
4 Hens (Kitchens)
8 Pro tem
9 Bow-wow
10 Scamp
11 Migrant
13 Fiji
15 Hog
16 Soda
18 Squeaky
20 Clean
23 Pedalo
24 Azalea
25 Tear
26 Digest

Down:
1 Karachi
2 Totem
3 Comb
5 Edwards
6 Swoon
7 Abridge
12 Chekhov
14 Ikebana
17 Dearest
19 Quest
21 Lease
22 Taxi

The Telegraph

Solutions 141–142

141

Across:
1 *Son*
3 *Daze*
5 *Cool* (Sunday School)
8 Old flame
10 Sync
11 Tie
13 Risen
14 All square
16 Dee
17 Ule
19 Expressed
21 Urban
22 Cru
24 Then
25 Awaiting
26 Duke
27 Swan
28 Ely

Down:
1 Soot
2 Nude
3 Delinquent
4 Zambia
6 Odysseus
7 Licensed
9 Lisle
12 Prevention
14 Adjusted
15 Leg break
18 Learn
20 Powwow
22 Cite
23 Ugly

142

Across:
1 *Flash*
4 *Gore*
8 *Don* (Flash Gordon)
9 Vassalage
10 Roux
11 Conjugal
12 Sow
13 Lackey
14 Asylum
16 Fit
17 Computer
18 Ruby
20 Conundrum
21 Zoo
22 Wept
23 Delve

Down:
1 Federal
2 Announcement
3 Hove
4 Go-slow
5 Readjust
6 Mangelwurzel
7 Bell
11 Coy
12 Sequence
14 Air
15 Maypole
16 Ferret
17 Cock
19 Amid

Solutions 143–144

143

Across:
1 Alley
4 Gaiter (Alligator)
9 Prairie
10 Blend
11 Crew
12 Article
13 Fox
14 Oral
16 Open
18 Pin
20 Enthuse
21 Asia
24 Delhi
25 Crusade
26 Earthy
27 Tenor

Down:
1 Aspect
2 Leave
3 York
5 Ambition
6 Treacle
7 Rudder
8 Relax
13 Flourish
15 Rattler
17 Meddle
18 Perch
19 Career
22 Stain
23 Curt

144

Across:
1 Error
4 Tick (Heretic)
8 Tap
9 Eyestrain
10 Amok
11 Stallion
12 Toy
13 Toucan
14 Useful
16 Art
17 Pitcairn
18 Scam
20 Abolition
21 Ion
22 Idle
23 Hints

Down:
1 Extract
2 Reproduction
3 Reed
4 Twenty
5 Catalyst
6 Satisfaction
7 Anon
11 Son
12 Tamarind
14 Urn
15 Laments
16 Arrive
17 Peat
19 Inch

The Telegraph

Solutions 145–146

145

Across:
1 Force
4 Height (Foresight)
7 Chatter
8 Duty
10 Loose
11 Enabled
14 Mane
16 Tested
18 Sledge
21 Date
23 Tempest
26 Split
27 Fang
28 Another
29 Streak
30 Sinks

Down:
1 Facilitate
2 Reasons
3 Extreme
4 Harden
5 India
6 Hotel
9 Adventures
12 Nest
13 Bye
15 Adds
17 Top
19 Lessons
20 Dolphin
22 Attack
24 Meant
25 Eagle

146

Across:
1 Full-page
5 Adze (Full-page ads)
8 Hireling
9 Isis
11 Campanology
14 Sum
16 Seize
17 Els
18 Adjustments
21 Bark
22 Alleluia
24 Lear
25 Portable

Down:
1 Fohn
2 Lyric
3 Palimpsest
4 Gun
6 Dispose
7 Essayist
10 Government
12 Axiom
13 Istanbul
15 Majorca
19 Squib
20 Wane
23 Leo

Solutions 147–148

147

Across:

1 Weighed
8 Bridge (Wadebridge)
9 Spotter
11 Rest room
12 Usual
14 Tend
15 Cornwall
17 Ennobled
18 Giro
20 Bacon
21 Aqueduct
23 Ease off
24 Cretan
25 Helotry

Down:

2 Expose
3 Gstaad
4 Ewer
5 Grating
6 Idiomatic
7 Vermilion
10 Redolence
12 Utterance
13 Uninjured
16 Abidjan
18 Gazebo
19 Roofer
22 Take

148

Across:

1 *Abba*
3 *Wrist*
7 *With* (Aberystwyth)
8 Tabernacle
9 Anew
12 Give and take
13 Tipsy
15 Ketch
19 Wheelbarrow
21 Rune
23 Amphibious
24 Agar
25 Three
26 Rosy

Down:

1 Altogether
2 Ageless
3 Waning
4 Incite
5 Tweak
6 Stye
10 Next
11 Wishy-washy
14 Pawn
16 Earlier
17 Temper
18 Oblige
20 Heart
22 Urge

Solutions 149–150

149

Across:
1 *Knot*
4 *Red*
6 *Harm* (Notre Dame)
8 Friend
9 Stress
10 Pedigree
11 Even
12 Prognosticate
17 Just
19 Terrible
22 Cinema
23 Shaggy
24 Jest
25 Try
26 Each

Down:
2 Nurse
3 Teeming
4 Rider
5 Descent
6 Horde
7 Respect
10 Pup
13 Routine
14 Outcast
15 Climate
16 Eye
18 Tweet
20 Risky
21 Logic

150

Across:
1 Canter
5 Loop (Canteloupe)
8 Gala
9 Calamity
10 Bishop
11 Bantam
12 Agriculture
15 Harass
17 Debate
19 Portrait
20 Avid
21 Dear
22 Riddle

Down:
2 Amati
3 Teacher
4 Recap
5 Lemon
6 Outrage
7 Global
12 Abalone
13 Casual
14 Upbraid
16 Alter
17 Deter
18 Trial

Also available from Hamlyn:

Telegraph All New Quick Crosswords £5.99

Volume 1: 978-0-600-62501-8

Volume 3: 978-0-600-62496-7 (publishing in September 2012)

Telegraph All New Big Book of Quick Crosswords £6.99

Volume 1: 978-0-600-62498-1 (publishing in September 2012)

Telegraph All New Toughie Crosswords £5.99

Volume 1: 978-0-600-62502-5

Volume 2: 978-0-600-62495-0 (publishing in September 2012)

Telegraph All New Cryptic Crosswords £5.99

Volume 1: 978-0-600-62468-4

Volume 2: 978-0-600-62500-1

Volume 3: 978-0-600-62499-8 (publishing in September 2012)

Telegraph All New Big Book of Cryptic Crosswords £6.99

Volume 1: 978-0-600-62467-7 (publishing in September 2012)

Telegraph All New Codewords £5.99

Volume 1: 978-0-600-62493-6

Telegraph General Knowledge Crosswords £5.99

Volume 1: 978-0-600-62497-4 (publishing in September 2012)

To order these or other Telegraph Books:

Call: 0844 871 1514
Visit: books.telegraph.co.uk
Post: Send cheques made payable to
Telegraph Books to the following address

Orders Dept
PO Box 582
Norwich
NR7 0GB

All UK orders will be subject to a 99p postage
and packing charge (call for overseas rates).
Products are supplied by and your contract is
with Bertrams Group Ltd not Telegraph Media
Group Limited.

For more puzzles go to
www.puzzles.telegraph.co.uk